THE TRANSIT OF VENUS

THE TRANSIT OF VENUS

The Quest to find the true Distance of the Sun

David Sellers

MagaVelda Press
2001

MAGAVELDA PRESS
38 Gledhow Wood Avenue
Leeds LS8 1NY
UK

Copyright © David Sellers 2001
First published by MagaVelda Press 2001

A CIP catalogue record for this book is available
from the British Library

ISBN 0-954 1013-0-8

Printed and bound in Great Britain by Antony Rowe Ltd, Chippenham

"Willingly would I burn to death like Phaeton, were this the price for reaching the Sun and learning its shape, its size, and its distance."
Eudoxus, Greek Mathematician and
Astronomer (c.408 – 355 BC)

CONTENTS

1   PROLOGUE: DUBLIN, 1882   9
2   WANDERING STARS   15
3   HEAVENLY SPHERES   28
4   THE SECRET OF THE PLANETS   45
5   '…THE SHAPES OF CYNTHIA…'   61
6   ORBITS AND TRANSITS   71
7   'A MOST AGREEABLE SPECTACLE'   75
8   PREDICTING TRANSITS OF VENUS   91
9   TO THE FOUR CORNERS OF THE EARTH   97
10 HALLEY'S ADMONITION   104
11 THE 1761 TRANSIT OF VENUS   119
12 'HAPPY IS OUR CENTURY…'   134
13 VENUS ABANDONED   155
14 VENUS RECLAIMED   167
15 THE COMING TRANSITS OF 2004 AND 2012   179

ACKNOWLEDGEMENTS   187
NOTES   188
MAP OF KEY PLACES   195
THE SOLAR PARALLAX   196
FURTHER READING   197
HALLEY'S FAMOUS EXHORTATION OF 1716   204
INDEX   218

CHAPTER 1

PROLOGUE
DUBLIN, 1882

Wednesday, 6th December 1882: Dublin awoke with a startled shiver. Snow! A dense curtain of snow, as far as the eye could see. As the morning progressed, conditions became worse. The normally bustling, clanging streets were subdued to a whisper. Along their margins stood forlorn lines of horse-drawn cabs, trapped by the white carpet settling in their midst. The premature arrival of winter had caught the city off-guard.

A furious gale swept through the streets, searching out every last yard and alley with its icy fingers, sending citizens scurrying to the warmth and shelter of their workplaces.

To the northwest of the city, exposed on the summit of a hill, was the Dunsink Observatory. Here, by contrast, the chill wind went unnoticed as it wrenched at the garments of a solitary figure who stood absorbed in contemplation. The lawn in front of the Observatory dome was already buried beneath a couple of inches of snow. The steps to the door were hardly discernible under the drifting snowflakes. Robert Ball seemed unaware of the cold grip of the wind and oblivious to the damp discomfort of his feet. His gaze never lingered on the ground. Instead it flitted anxiously between the leaden sky and the dome.

In more clement circumstances, this simple dome, a hemispherical roof perched on a small cylindrical building, had become the focus of his life. Since being appointed Astronomer Royal of Ireland, he had dedicated himself to an exhausting nightly round of observations. Here, on cloud-free occasions, he would often be found at 3 o'clock in the morning, still peering through the telescope. His mission was to detect and chart tiny seasonal changes in the positions of the stars.

This day was to be different. He had been looking forward to it for longer than he cared to remember. So it was with furrowed brow that he paused to glance skyward. The storm clouds looked set to ruin everything. Circumstances could hardly have been less hopeful for the great astronomical event—a 'Transit of Venus'—which he anticipated. In the early hours of the afternoon the planet Venus would begin a very rare passage in front of the Sun. If the skies cleared, Venus would be visible in splendid silhouette against the solar disc. So rare was the event, it had occurred only three times since it was first witnessed by an English youth, Jeremiah Horrocks, two and a half centuries previously. True, Horrocks too had been beset by clouds. Astronomers had long learned to be fatalistic about the weather. But snow? Ball could not believe his bad luck.

Even with clear skies there would be only a brief sight of Venus. The transit would last for several hours, but from Dublin only the commencement would be visible. Shortly afterwards, this curious spectacle would be lost in the sunset.

Inside the observatory the equipment lay ready. In the centre stood a superb equatorial telescope. Attached to the eyepiece of the telescope, especially for this day's observations, was a device to dim the expected brilliance of the Sun to viewable proportions. Looking at the undimmed Sun through a telescope would cause instant and permanent blindness. Ball reflected wistfully on the naive optimism embodied in such precautions, which seemed in the event to be a mere mockery. The sky was totally overcast and any hope of seeing the Sun

South Dome at Dunsink

was all but extinguished. Nevertheless, he exhorted his staff to make all their preparations 'precisely as they would have done were the Sun shining with undimmed splendour.' [1]

The previous day he had gone through a 'full-dress rehearsal', pointing the telescope to the Sun, and following it down to the position in which it would be at the time of the transit on the following day. To his horror, he had found that the Sun, on the transit evening, would set directly behind a tree, situated on neighbouring land. Not every neighbour would have readily agreed this to be a problem, but, happily, the tree's owner, on being told that it stood between the Dunsink Observatory and the transit of Venus, had had it chopped down forthwith.

On the transit day, at 11 o'clock in the morning Ball and his assistants set to work. Six tons of rotating dome rumbled into the correct position. A flurry of snow entered as the shutter was opened. Still the clouds were impenetrable. With an assistant operating the handle, the eighteen-foot long telescope was slowly turned to point at that part of the sky where the Sun should have been. The clockwork mechanism then took over, causing the telescope to lock onto this part of the sky and gradually to revolve as the invisible Sun was doing.

The predicted time of the transit arrived ... and passed. Still no sign of the Sun. The tension eased as hope waned. Ball sighed and, rubbing his hands to keep warm, looked sadly at the gleaming instrument before him. At the heart of this telescope was an excellent 12-inch diameter object glass. In his mind's eye, he pictured the crisp image of Venus which could have been offered by it, if only the clouds had cleared. This was no ordinary glass, let it be known. It had previously belonged to the celebrated double-star observer, Sir James South (1785–1867). Made in Paris around 1830, purchased by South, then smuggled out of France, it had been at the centre of a bitter four-year lawsuit between South and the London-based firm who had been commissioned to make the mounting. South lost the case and, in a fit of rage, he had publicly smashed the mounting to pieces and auctioned off the bits. Fortunately, he saved the object glass—at the time, one of the largest in the world—and, shortly before his death, he donated it to the Board of Trinity College Dublin, from where it had found its way to Dunsink.

Ball's attention returned to the weather. At first it appeared unchanged, but suddenly his most earnest hopes were gratified: 'Just as I had begun to despair, an almost miraculous improvement took place in the weather. The sky lightened, the Sun burst forth behind that very place where the tree had stood the day before, and then, to my delight, I beheld the globe of the planet Venus standing out on the solar disc.' [2]

It was almost two o'clock in the afternoon. A small notch in the margin of the Sun showed that the transit had commenced and a full third of the planet was already upon the Sun.

The observers stood transfixed. Meanwhile, the snow continued. 'While steadily looking at the exquisitely beautiful sight of the gradual advance of the planet', Ball recounted, 'I became aware that there were other objects besides Venus between me and the sun. They were the snowflakes: which again began to fall rapidly. I will admit the phenomenon was singularly beautiful. The telescopic effect of a snowstorm with the sun as a background I had never seen before.' [3]

Amidst the swirling snow, the image faded in and out of view. The observers were surprised by their own reaction to the sight. 'We had only obtained a brief view', said Ball, 'and we had not yet been able to make any measurements or other observations that could be of service. Still, to have seen even a part of a transit of Venus is an event to remember for a lifetime, and we felt more delight than can easily be expressed at even this slight gleam of success.' [4]

The poor weather conditions mercifully abated and the clarity of the round silhouette, now starkly visible part way across the Sun, steadily improved. The professional astronomer in Ball took over. He and his assistants made repeated measurements of the changing position of Venus. Each measurement, taken against cross-wires in the eyepiece of the telescope, was carefully timed with the observatory clock.

They were fortunate. The day of the transit coincided with violent gales from the northeast, accompanied by snowstorms throughout Britain. Places as far apart as Dublin, Aberdeen and the Channel Islands were all affected. Telegraphic communications were severed. Tramways and trains ceased to run. At least three ships were sunk off the English coast. At the Royal Greenwich Observatory the whole of the staff was ready at the instruments, but, due to cloud, not even the Sun could be discerned, let alone Venus. Hardly anyone in the country made such extensive observations as the Dunsink observers.

They did not have long to enjoy the spectacle. It was wintertime: days were short. Before the afternoon was through, Ball reluctantly conceded that '... the sun was now getting low, the clouds again began to interfere, and we saw that the pursuit of the transit must be left to the thousands of astronomers in happier climes who had been eagerly awaiting it…The sun was already beginning to put on the ruddy hues of sunset, and there, far in on its face, was the sharp, round, black disc of Venus. It was then easy to sympathise with the supreme joy of Horrocks, when, in 1639, he for the first time witnessed this spectacle. The intrinsic interest of the phenomenon, its rarity, the fulfillment of the prediction, the noble problem which the transit of Venus helps us to solve, are all present to our thoughts when we look at this pleasing picture, a repetition of which will not occur again until the flowers are blooming in the June of AD 2004.' [5]

In the quiet isolation of the Dunsink Observatory, Robert Ball knew that he was not alone in observing the transit. His expectation that 'thousands of astronomers in happier climes' would be watching, however, understated the situation. The transit of Venus had captured the imagination of astronomers and public alike. Ball's professional counterparts observed with expensive telescopes, but many people watched through fragments of smoked glass. Across the entire sunlit portion of the Earth the sight of the transit was eagerly awaited and, once under way, it engendered the same awe in all who watched. This was the sight, which in the previous century had lured intrepid expeditions,

Robert Ball

including the famous one of Captain Cook, to far-flung corners of the globe. Now, in a more enlightened age, millions had been alerted to the event.

The 'noble problem which the transit of Venus helps us to solve' was nothing less than the determination of the distance to the Sun, the sizing of the Solar System and the measurement of the Universe itself. By 1882, more effective ways had been found to gauge the distance of the Sun, but in the eighteenth century the transit of Venus had been the key which unlocked the secret of the Sun's distance for the first time.

Almost every educated person *knows* that the Sun is 93 million miles (or 150 million kilometres) away. This is an immense distance: so immense that it is virtually beyond comprehension. Perhaps it is precisely *because* the figure is so incredible that most people are prepared to take it on trust, without batting an eyelid: a pity, because *how* we know is often far more fascinating than *what* we know.

The quest to find the Sun's distance—the so-called 'Astronomical Unit'—runs like a bright thread through the entire tapestry of astronomical history. Its story spans two millennia and reveals the extraordinary efforts which have been devoted to discovering the true place of our earthly home in the solar system. It also shows the crucial role played by the transit of Venus in this endeavour. This rare and spectacular event did not occur at all during the twentieth century and when it occurs in 2004, not one soul will be living who observed the last one in 1882.

CHAPTER 2

WANDERING STARS

By the time he saw the 1882 transit of Venus, Robert Ball (1840–1913) had already become the most accomplished populariser of astronomy in the British Isles. Mixing wit and scientific acumen with clear exposition and a booming voice, he held audiences in thrall. The transit of Venus was dear to his heart. It had been the subject of his very first public lecture, delivered eight years earlier, in Birmingham.

Following the success of this lecture, Ball toured the length and breadth of the country, speaking on related themes. Even in the smallest towns, the halls and meeting rooms would be filled to capacity with people eager to hear him speak. The brief entry in his diary for 7th January 1890 after his visit to a small Yorkshire town was typical: 'Audience of 1,000. Many turned away.'[1] The obituary published by the Royal Society after his death reckoned that, over the years, he must have lectured to more than one million people: an astonishing achievement, in the years before mass media.

Public interest in astronomy, partly awoken by the Venus transit, seemed insatiable. Another leading astronomer, the Jesuit priest Father Stephen Perry (1833–1889), found a similar situation as he went on speaking tours of northern England. Perry, a veteran of the British Expedition sent to the remote Kerguelen Island to observe the 1874 transit of Venus, found large audiences, eager to learn. At one of his talks, in Wigan, over 3,000 turned up! In 1884 he gave a series of twelve lectures in Liverpool at which the average attendance was over one thousand.

This was the age of 'self-improvement'. Countless citizens, previously untouched by any formal education, save the most elementary kind, yearned to know more about the world in which they lived.

As the lecture hall lamps dimmed and light began to stream through the 'magic lantern' slides, audiences were introduced to the marvelous discoveries of nineteenth century Astronomy: a new planet; spiral nebulae; the physical nature of the stars, revealed by analysis of their light. Even the distance and speed of some of our nearest stellar neighbours had been well established.

In the course of the lecture, the current state of knowledge would be compared and contrasted with the earliest notions of humankind. To appreciate where Astronomy had arrived at, it was essential to know where it had comefrom.

Curiously, the ideas developed in Antiquity to explain the heavens are probably the easiest to sympathise with. They are the ones which, at first glance, seem to accord most naturally with everyday experience and to fit in with our intuition. Unfortunately, they were wrong. Only by seeing how they were ultimately *proven* to be wrong, can we understand how it became possible to measure the distance of the Sun.

When the earliest observers gazed up at the sky, they assumed that everything in that sky revolved around *their* world. Nothing could have been more natural: it was the most obvious interpretation of what they were seeing. Every day the Sun rose in the east and soared across the sky to set in the west. The Moon too and all the glittering stars made the same journey, day after day. At night the sky took on the appearance of a huge starry dome, majestically revolving about the Earth.

With each successive night, any particular star rose a little earlier, above the eastern horizon, but the positions of the stars relative to each other remained fixed. Each star always rose and set at the same place on the eastern and western horizons. Everything conspired to give the firm impression that the stars were really fixed to some great unseen dome and were thereby bound into this eternal gyration about the Earth.

Ancient civilisations imagined vast arrays of mythical creatures and other shapes to match the arbitrary, but enduring, patterns of stars which were perceived in the sky. The sky served them as a storybook—a celestial substitute for the written word—as myths and legends were assigned to the constellations. More importantly, many ancient astronomers also applied themselves to recording the changes which they saw in the sky over long periods. Logs of astronomical observations made in Babylonia as long ago as the second millenium BC have survived to this day on tablets of stone and clay. Through them, we start to catch a faint glimpse of the remarkable level of knowledge possessed by star-gazers in the distant past. In these logs we see the motions of the Sun and Moon laid bare, and we see also that our early ancestors had come to realise that not quite all stars were fixed.

The star trails in a two and a half hour exposure photograph centred on the north pole star clearly show the rotation of the night sky

It is with this realisation, that our present story really begins. Five 'stars', and five alone, appeared to change position relative to the others. Each night they would generally appear to have shifted a little further eastward, compared with the constellations. These were not dim, unimportant stars—the supporting cast in the grand spectacle. Quite the contrary: after the Moon, they were at times the brightest objects in the night sky. For some, the change of position could be noticed only over a period of weeks or months; for others, it could be seen even between one night and the next. The ancient Greeks knew them as *planetai*—or 'wandering stars'. Whenever visible, they always seemed to be following roughly the same path in the sky as the Sun. To us, they are the planets: Mercury, Venus, Mars, Jupiter and Saturn (Neptune, Uranus and Pluto had not yet been discovered).

It would be a long time before the true nature of these planets could be known. Along the route to this knowledge, the first milestone was an understanding of the Earth itself and its relationship to its neighbour, the Moon.

Progress was uneven. In the Middle Ages, many sailors feared falling off the edge of the world if they ventured too far. And yet, even as early as 500 BC, advanced thinkers in Greece were well aware that the Earth was a sphere. They knew that the look-out on a ship's mast could see signals from the shore which couldn't be seen by a sailor on deck. Even a child playing on the sea-shore knew how a ship seemed to disappear beneath the horizon as it sailed out to sea. With a heroic leap of the imagination, both facts were taken as evidence that the Earth's surface was spherical.

The Earth and Moon as seen from the Galileo spacecraft, clearly showing spherical shapes *(Photo: NASA)*

How hard it is now for us, who have been reared on the truism that the Earth is round, to appreciate the difficulty which the ancients must have had in accepting this. The 'sphere' idea seemed to contradict common-sense. It took an act of faith to believe it: faith in simple observations and the bold application of the intellect.

How easy it is to accept a familiar sight—like the ship sinking beneath the horizon—without a second glance. But, familiarity breeds contempt and the meaning of the sight passes unnoticed. In the same way, most people accept the changing phases of the Moon without a thought as to what is implied by them. Not so the true scientist: many of the greatest revelations of science have been born out of questioning the commonplace.

Thus, the philosopher Anaxagoras (c.500–428 BC), pondering over the phases of the Moon, wondered why its bright side always faced the Sun. He was driven to conclude that: 'The Sun places the brightness in the Moon.' [2] Moonlight was the reflected light of the Sun.

Anaxagoras did not let the matter rest there. His every waking hour was devoted to mulling over such issues. Indeed, when someone asked him what was the object of being born, he replied: 'The investigation of the Sun, Moon and heaven.' [3] Having worked out that the Sun provided the light of the Moon, he was able to move on to further startling conclusions. Witness the first century historian Aëtius: 'Anaxagoras…held that…the eclipses of the Moon were caused by its falling within the shadow of the Earth, which then comes between the Sun and the Moon, while eclipses of the Sun were due to the interposition of the Moon.' [4] For the first time, there started to emerge, a picture of the Earth, Moon and Sun as a *system*.

Aristotle (384–322 BC), Greek philosopher, and one time teacher of Alexander the Great, built upon this picture. Not only was the Earth spherical, so too, he claimed, was the Moon. 'Were it any other shape, it would not appear crescent-shaped or gibbous during the greater part of its waxing and waning, and only at one moment semi-circular.' [5] The phases of the Moon, Aristotle correctly observed, were simply due to the changed view of the sunlit side that we get as the Moon orbits the Earth.

Aristotle

Every 29½ days we have a 'new' Moon, when the sunlit side is facing entirely away from the Earth. The Moon consequently disappears from view. At the opposite side of its orbit, we see the whole of the sunlit side and the Moon is said

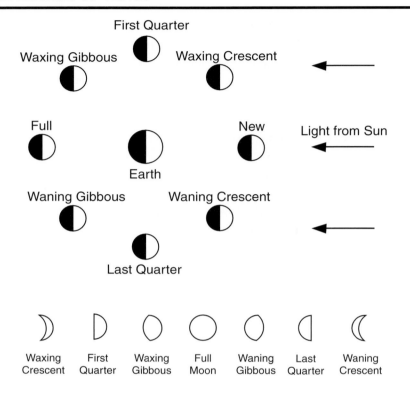

Aristotle's explanation of the Moon's phases

to be 'full'. At intermediate positions we see a crescent or gibbous Moon, as illustrated above.

It is not unusual to find adults who think that the Moon is solely a feature of the night sky and have not noticed that the Moon is often visible at the same time as the Sun! Aristotle's explanation showed quite clearly why this happens.

The arrangement of the Earth-Moon system, proposed by Aristotle, was capable of yielding more than just an explanation of the Moon's phases. To the inquisitive mind, it also held clues about the amount by which the distance of the Sun exceeded that of the Moon.

This was just the point taken up by another Greek thinker, Aristarchus of Samos (c.320–c.250 BC). In his celebrated book, *On the Sizes and Distances of the Sun and the Moon*, he revealed how knowledge of this system could permit deduction of the distance of the Sun itself.

His method was remarkable for its simplicity. Taking as his starting point the now familiar assumption that 'the Moon shines by the light of the Sun', Aristarchus surmised that 'when the Moon appears to us halved, the great circle which divides the dark and the bright portions of the Moon is in the direction of our eye.' [6] If, at this moment, threads were stretched out to link the Earth, Moon and Sun, as shown in the figure below, they would form a very slender right-angled triangle, SEM. Aristarchus knew that, if the angle between the lines of sight to the Moon (EM) and Sun (ES) could be measured, then the ratio of the distances to the Sun and Moon could be readily deduced. The larger the angle, the larger the ratio*.

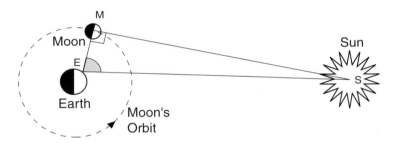

Aristarchus' method of finding the relative distances of the Sun and Moon (for the sake of clarity, distances and sizes are grossly distorted)

The method was put to the test. From observations made with all the care which could be mustered, he estimated 'that, when the moon appears to us halved, its distance from the sun is less than a quadrant [90°] by one-thirtieth part of a quadrant.' [7] [in other words, the angle (SEM) between the Moon and the Sun is 87°]

His verdict was that 'the distance of the sun from the earth is greater than eighteen times, but less than twenty times, the distance of the moon from the earth.' [8]

So, how far *was* the Moon? Aristarchus provided an ingenious method of answering that question too. One evening, on the occasion of a total eclipse

* $\cos SEM = EM/ES$

of the Moon, he set about carefully timing the event. Like Anaxagoras, he too was aware that an eclipse of the Moon is caused by the Moon passing through the Earth's shadow. This eclipse had a particularly long duration, so it was clear that the Moon was passing right through the centre of the Earth's shadow.

As soon as the Moon made contact with the Earth's shadow, he began timing. He discovered that the time taken for the leading edge of the Moon to progress from one side of the shadow to the other, was twice as long as the time which had been required for the Moon's full diameter to slide into the shadow. The conclusion was obvious: at the distance of the Moon, the Earth's shadow was 'two Moons' wide.

So what? Sometimes, far-reaching conclusions flow from simple observations. This was a case in point. There were only two 'hard facts' to go on—namely, that the Earth's shadow was 'two Moons' wide, and also that the Moon appeared the same size as the Sun, even though the latter was 19 times further away. Armed with these seemingly meagre scraps of information, and some elementary geometry, it was possible for the contemporaries of Aristarchus to calculate the distances. The Earth itself served as their yardstick. The answers surpassed, in enormity, anything which they might have pre-supposed. The Moon was about 80 Earth semi-diameters away and, therefore, the distance of the Sun was approximately 1500 Earth semi-diameters. The maths was flawless. Unfortunately, the distance for the Sun, impressively large though it was, turned out to be far wide of the mark. It should have been at least fifteen times larger!

What had let them down was the first step, when Aristarchus had measured the angle between the Sun and the half-Moon. In practice, it is very difficult to gauge exactly when the edge of the Moon's shadow—the *terminator*—is at the half-way point: after all, the Moon's surface is rough and the shadow does not follow a perfectly straight line. The true value of the angle which Aristarchus set at 87° is actually almost 89°50', thus making the Sun's distance 344 times that of the Moon, not 19 times. Although his figure was much too small, Aristarchus at least provided the first well-founded indication that the Sun was an extraordinarily distant object.

Notice that he measured the distance between celestial objects in terms of angles. Admittedly, his angular measures seem unfamiliar: he uses fractions of quadrants, instead of our degrees. Even so, he illustrated an important point about describing the observed separation between objects in the sky. It is no good holding an outstretched hand to the sky and declaring that two stars are 'a hand's breadth' away from each other. Who's hand? How long an arm? The only unambiguous way to give the separation is to state their differences in direction—in other words, the angle between them. Our normal units for measuring angles are degrees (°). One complete rotation is 360 degrees (or 360°); each degree can be sub-divided into 60 minutes (often written as 60 arc-minutes, or 60'); each minute can be further sub-divided into 60 seconds (60 arc-seconds, or 60").

For the Greek astronomers, like Aristarchus, who accepted the sphericity of the Earth, the most intriguing question of all was: how big was the sphere? 'I believe', said Socrates, Plato's hero, 'that the Earth is very large, and that we who dwell between the Pillars of Hercules and the river Phasis live in a small part of it about the sea, like ants or frogs about a pond.' [9] The Earth's surface seemed endless, no matter how far one traveled. Socrates also knew that the Earth would have to be extremely large in order to create the illusion of a flat surface upon which everyday life is conducted. It was hard to imagine how something so large as this could possibly be measured. Nevertheless, out of the searing heat of southern Egypt, came an observational morsel which provided a simple way of doing just that. It came by way of a library in Alexandria on the north African coast,

By the middle of the third century BC, Alexandria had become a focal point of Greek scholarship. It's Great Library, founded by the ruler, Ptolemy Soter, was looked upon as one of the wonders of the ancient world. The Library's aim was to assemble a collection of the entire body of Greek literature. Ships' captains sailing from Alexandria were instructed to bring back scrolls from every port of call.

Librarianship was taken seriously: Ptolemy Evergetes, one of the successors of the Library's founder, made a practice of having every visitor to Alexandria searched before they were allowed to enter the city. Any book found on them, or in their bags, would be confiscated and copied onto papyrus. The copy would be given to the bewildered owner and the original would be placed in the Library. Ultimately, a staggering half million volumes were amassed, covering every field of knowledge. Sadly, the Library and most of its contents were destroyed by wars.

Long, long before that calamity, the Library had as its director the geographer, Eratosthenes (c.276–195 BC) of Cyrene (now Shahhat, Libya). He was known to his contemporaries as a 'Jack of all trades'—a *pentathlos*—and, by implication maybe, a 'master of none'. Today, Eratosthenes cuts an altogether more imposing figure than his critical colleagues. Whether his writings were amongst those destroyed, along with the Library, is not known. His ideas and discoveries have come down to us, not through his own words, but through the accounts of other authors, such as the astronomer Cleomedes. It is in this way that we know of his important chance find.

Eratosthenes had learned an intriguing fact relating to the southern Egyptian town of Syene—near modern day Aswan. At midday, on the longest day of the year, the Sun cast no shadows at Syene. In fact, so a later embellishment of the story goes, the Sun's direct reflection could be seen in the water at the bottom of a deep well in the town. Anyone who dared to look down the well would be blinded by the light. The Sun, at this moment, therefore had to be vertically above Syene. In Alexandria to the north at the same time, however, as Eratosthenes knew from his own experience, the shadow cast on a sundial was displaced from the vertical by an angle equal to one fiftieth of a complete circle. Therefore, he concluded, the distance between Syene and Alexandria must be one fiftieth of the Earth's

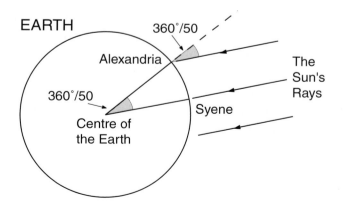

Eratosthenes' method of measuring the Earth's circumference

circumference. He had no means of directly measuring the distance between the two towns, but from travelers' estimates of the time taken to trek between them, he estimated that their separation was 5000 stades. Hence, the Earth's circumference was 250,000 stades and its radius, or semi-diameter, was roughly one-third of that figure.

No one can be certain how good an estimate this was. The exact length of the stade, in modern units of measure, is not known. Some modern authorities put the conversion of 250,000 stades at 39,900 kilometres: almost unbelievably close to the correct figure—40,074 kilometres—for the circumference of the Earth. Whatever the true value of the stade, it does seem probable that Eratosthenes would have obtained a reasonable value for the Earth's size using this method.

The 'Well of Eratosthenes' has never been found. Did it really exist? In 1914, this photograph, purporting to show the famous well, was published in the astronomical journal *The Observatory*. It drew a scathing rebuke from the renowned astronomer-historian J.L.E. Dreyer. He pointed out that only Cleomedes (c.50 BC) had given a detailed account of Eratosthenes' experiment, and that account did not mention a well. There had been allusions to such a well in the writings of Strabo and Pliny, but these made no mention of Eratosthenes.

Thus, a vital step had been taken in the mission to size the solar system. The radius of the Earth was the yardstick for measuring the heavens and now, at least in rough terms, the size of that yardstick had been determined. Aristarchus had permitted astronomers to give the Sun's distance as 1500 Earth semi-diameters. Eratosthenes had now enabled that distance to be translated into practical units of measure—stades. But the Earth's semi-diameter, as a yardstick, could be used in a much more sophisticated way. How? Essentially, by utilising a very simple, age-old surveying technique: *triangulation.*

To explain this, let us imagine ourselves looking down on the Earth, from above the North Pole, at a time when the Earth is at its mean distance from the Sun. Then let us imagine an observer, on the Equator at A, seeing the Sun on the horizon, as shown below.

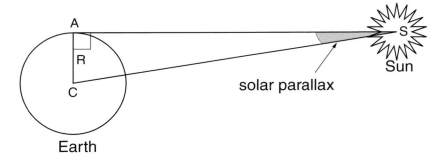

The angle ASC is the solar parallax and *CS= R/sin(solar parallax)*
(the Earth's size is greatly exaggerated relative to the Sun)

Our observer's line of sight to the Sun's centre is not in quite the same direction as the line from the centre of the Earth to the Sun's centre. This is the parallax effect. Looking at an object from a slightly different vantage point seems to shift its position. The effect can be clearly seen if we look at a nearby object—say a finger, held at arm's length—first with one eye and then with the other. The object appears to shift from side to side, relative to more distant things. It's direction differs according to which eye we use.

In the same way, the line of sight to the Sun from point A in the diagram appears to converge with that from point C. The further away the Sun, compared with the radius of the Earth, the smaller the angle of convergence seems to be. This angle is called the *solar parallax*. It can also be described as *the angular semi-diameter of the Earth as seen from the Sun.*

Look again at the triangle formed by points ASC in the diagram. The length of the side AC is equal to the Earth's radius. The angle at A is a right angle—in other words, 90 degrees. If we can find out the size of the shaded angle, at S, the *solar parallax*, then, without leaving the Earth, we will be able to work out the length of side CS: the distance of the Sun—also known as one Astronomical Unit.

Unfortunately, such an exceedingly small angle as the solar parallax is difficult to measure. The difficulty is compounded by the nature of the Sun itself. In the simplest procedure, the parallax of a celestial body could be discerned as a slight angular shift when the body is observed from widely separated locations. With the Sun though, such is its brilliance, no background stars are visible in the sky, against which any such shift may be gauged.

In ancient times, every astronomer of note grappled with this problem, but to little avail. No direct method of solution existed. The route to the conquest of the solar parallax—and thereby the Sun's distance—would have to be indirect and devious. It would have to involve astronomical instruments with an accuracy that Aristotle could not even have begun to dream about. It would also involve an interpretation of heavenly movements radically different from that to which Aristotle clung.

CHAPTER 3

HEAVENLY SPHERES

The Cause of Night

'Night covers the earth with its vast pall of darkness, either because the sun, on reaching the furthest verge of the sky at the end of his long journey, in exhaustion breathes out his fires, impaired by their travels and weakened by the mass of air which they have traversed; or because the same force that carried the solar disk above the earth, impels it to change course and pass beneath the earth.'

On the Nature of Things, Lucretius (99-55 BC)

It is easy to smile at the false theories put forward by the Roman poet, Lucretius, as an explanation for nightfall and the motion of the Sun. [1] In his day however, this kind of reasoning seemed quite sophisticated. So much of nature was a puzzle. There were plenty of openings for a philosopher's power of speculation to be gainfully employed. Alas, emotionally satisfying though the explanations were, they had little connection with reality. To elucidate the true reason for the apparent movements of the Sun, Moon and stars, honest enquirers would have to reject speculation and learn the shape of the heavens, through careful observation and measurement.

Easier said than done! To ancient peoples the sky was unfathomable. The stars were a mystery. What magical force held them aloft? How far away were they? Were they all at the same distance?

The night sky's more sporadic visitors, such as comets, were a particularly thorny problem. To the ancients, the starry vault above the Earth was unchanging and, therefore, comets could not be true members of the celestial family. That is why Aristotle had these lingering vagrants marked down as atmospheric spectacles—certainly closer than the Moon.

In antiquity, with few exceptions, philosophers accepted the view of the universe put forward by Aristotle. Accordingly, the heavens were 'free from disturbance, change and external influence' [2] and consisted of the Sun, Moon, planets and stars, revolving in circles about a stationary Earth. They were constrained to move in these circles by a system of concentric spheres—one within the other, like the skins of an onion. Some ancient astronomers saw the spheres as being somewhat like 'permitted paths', but Aristotle imagined them as real, mechanical entities, holding up the objects which they enclosed: stopping them from falling to Earth. Obviously, the spheres themselves could not be seen and the inner spheres did not obstruct the view of objects held by the outer spheres. Therefore, he concluded that the spheres were completely transparent or crystalline.

The order of the spheres, as one moved outward from the Earth, was based on the apparent swiftness of motion of each body—planet, Sun or Moon—in a westerly direction: The swifter bodies being judged further from the Earth. 'It is found that their several movements, in so far as some are quicker and others slower, correspond to their distances', claimed Aristotle. '… it is our hypothesis that the outermost revolution of the heaven [the stars] is simple and is the swiftest, while those of the other heavenly bodies are slower and have more than one component, for each of them moves, in a sense contrary to the motion of the heavens.' [3] Consequently, the accepted sequence was: the Moon, Mercury, Venus, the Sun, Mars, Jupiter and Saturn. Forming the background to the movements of all of these was the sphere of the fixed stars—the *'eighth heaven'*.

Aristotle speculated that the greater distance of the stars was also evidenced by another fact: '…our sight, when at long range, wavers on account of its weakness. This is perhaps the reason why the stars, which are fastened (to the sphere), appear to twinkle, while the planets do not twinkle; for the planets are near, so that the visual ray when it reaches them is within its powers, whereas, when directed to the fixed stars, it quivers on account of the distance, being strained too far.' [4] He was barking up the wrong tree. There is no such thing as a 'visual ray': nothing passes from our eyes to the

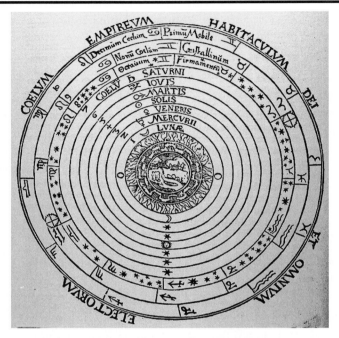

**The Earth-centred universe of Aristotle, showing the
crystal spheres for each planet, from Peter Apian's
Cosmographia (1539)**

stars. He was right of course about the stars being further than the planets, but it was a case of the right answer, for the wrong reasons.

To Aristotle's contemporaries, and many generations following, his plan of the universe had a satisfying uniformity about it. Everything moved in circles. Every celestial body maintained its fixed and proper distance from the Earth. And circular motion, as Aristotle was fond of reminding his public, was an aspect of perfection: the natural behaviour of bodies predestined to move in an endlessly repeating path.

Unfortunately, this theory was not too hot when tested against the evidence of astronomers' own eyes. The planets in particular seemed to have subtler motions, which did not fit in with Aristotle's spheres. The planets were subject to marked changes of brightness. It was as if they were advancing towards and receding away from the Earth: not the sort of change one would see if they were confined to a circular orbit centred on the Earth.

The biggest headache for Aristotelians was *retrograde motion*. Although planets generally moved in an eastward direction against the background of fixed stars, there was sometimes an unaccountable backward—or 'retrograde'—motion, from east to west. No simple Earth-centred model, based on concentric circles, could explain such fickleness. Another difficulty was that the motion of Venus and Mercury never seemed to carry them far from the Sun. Venus is never more than 47°, or so, to the east or west of the Sun and therefore is only ever seen a few hours before sunrise or a few hours after sunset. Mercury is an even more faithful companion of the Sun: never departing by more than 27° to either side.

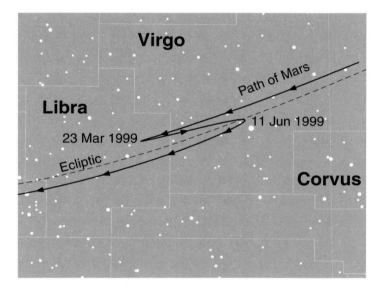

The retrograde motion of Mars amongst the stars (1999)

One man's explanation for these features of planetary motion reigned supreme for almost one half of recorded history. Over the course of 1400 years, Claudius Ptolemy (c.90–170) was revered as the ultimate authority on the movements of the heavenly bodies. His book, the *Almagest* had a remarkably enduring influence. In its thirteen volumes, Ptolemy presented a series of geometrical arrangements which was able to account for the observed positions of the planets, whilst not totally abandoning Aristotle's Earth-centred structure of the Universe.

Ptolemy was born in the Nile Valley in Egypt, probably in the early first century AD. His writings are in Greek and are firmly part of the Greek scientific tradition. His life however is a complete blank. We do not know where he lived, when he was born or when he died. A clue is given by his observations, which are recorded in the *Almagest*. All are from Alexandria, between the years 127 AD and 141 AD. Historians have speculated that he worked at the Great Library of Alexandria. He was certainly a scholar of great eminence in his own lifetime and it seems highly likely that the Library would have been a good place to look for him.

Claudius Ptolemy *(Courtesy of Prof. Owen Gingerich)*

In his explanation of a planet's motion, Ptolemy stuck to circular orbits about the Earth, but allowed the Earth itself to be slightly displaced from the centre of the circle. He also introduced the *epicycle*: a small circular motion of the planet, superimposed on the main circular orbit about the Earth. Thus, the centre of the epicycle was in uniform motion around the main circle, but, at any given moment, the planet in question might be ahead of or behind the centre of the epicycle, as seen from the Earth. In moving from a position *ahead* to a position *behind*, the observed retrograde motion could be reproduced.

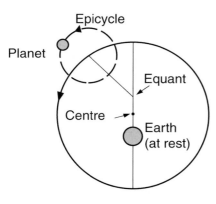

The epicycle of Ptolemy

To some, the epicycle was an abomination: an unacceptable departure from the perfection of Aristotle's simple spheres. Ptolemy himself did not *necessarily* imagine the epicycle to represent the true physical path of a

THE EPICYCLE AND EQUANT

The epicycle device alone did not sufficiently explain the motion of the planets. The speed of the planets as they wove their way among the fixed stars needed a further correction. Ptolemy provided this with a geometrical construct known as the *equant*. Basically, this meant the introduction of a point which was offset from the centre of the main circle and letting it be about this point that the epicycle's centre orbited, at a constant speed. Thus, seen by an observer at the equant, the motion of a planet's epicycle would seem to be uniform, but seen from the Earth it would sometimes speed up or slow down, which was indeed the actual appearance.

The epicycle and other geometrical devices assigned to the Moon by Ptolemy, in order to account for its position against the background stars, reveal an interesting aspect of his thinking. If taken literally for the path of the Moon, they would have the Moon at times halving its distance from the Earth: inevitably making it appear to double in size - which is clearly contrary to the evidence of our eyes. It is inconceivable that an astronomer of Ptolemy's stature would not know this. The only conclusion we can draw is that he did not reckon the epicycle, at least in this case, to be other than a calculating device.

planet. In all likelihood, he deemed it simply as a calculating tool, with which to determine how the speed of a planet varied in the course of its orbit. The question of the *cause* of the variations did not arise.

To modern minds it seems strange that someone as smart as Ptolemy could dream up these complex patterns of motion without considering how such motion could be brought about. We must remember however, that, this was many centuries before Isaac Newton's Law of Universal Gravitation had been propounded. No one had a truly practical explanation for *any kind* of orbit. The challenge facing astronomers was not to *explain* planetary motion, but to *accurately describe* it. Besides which, Ptolemy was convinced that his representation of the heavenly movements appeared complicated only because of the limitations of the mathematics and analogies at his disposal: 'One must not think that these hypotheses are too elaborate just because our technical devices are inadequate. It would be wrong to compare human contrivances with things divine.' [5]

What about night and day? Here, Ptolemy and Aristotle were at one. Although a few astronomers had had the temerity to suggest that night and day were caused by the Earth spinning eastward, Ptolemy and Aristotle saw the idea as preposterous. After all, if the Earth were spinning, said Ptolemy, then the huge speed of its surface would result in any loose objects being swept along to the west: 'Neither clouds nor other flying or thrown objects would ever be seen moving towards the east, since the earth's motion towards the east would always outrun and overtake them.' [6]

The maxim of ancient Greek science was that any theory should 'save the appearances'. In other words, the predictions given by a theory should conform with all the observed facts. Judged purely and simply in this light, Ptolemy's model of the universe was an outstanding success. The error concerning night and day made no difference to its predictions of what would actually be seen in the sky.

Ptolemy knew that he had fashioned a tool of unprecedented power. He sensed that the harmony between its predictions and the real movements of the planets had put him in communion with the heavens. 'I know that I am mortal and the creature of a day; but when I search out the massed wheeling circles of the stars, my feet no longer touch the earth, but, side by side with Zeus himself, I take my fill of ambrosia, the food of the gods.' [7]

From the time of the Roman Emperor Hadrian (76–138) until the European Renaissance in the sixteenth century, the work of Ptolemy went unchallenged. It appeared to provide all the answers that were required in relation to the movement of the sky and everything therein.

In the eighth and ninth centuries most of the key Greek scientific works—the *Almagest* included—were translated into Arabic. This is the origin of the title *Almagest*. The original Greek title of Ptolemy's work was *Megiste Syntaxis* (The Greatest Construction). The Arabs translated this as *Al Magisti*. It is by a corrupted version of this name, *Almagest*, that we know the book today.

Baghdad, in Iraq, became a latter-day Alexandria: one of the world's great centres of learning. There, under the patronage of Great Caliphs, such as Harun al-Rashid (786–809) and al-Ma'mum (813–833), the translation of mathematical and scientific texts became almost a sacred quest. A translation unit, combined with a library and academy, the 'House of Wisdom', was established to take on the task systematically. Throughout the Dark Ages, Arab scholars kept the flame of science tended, whilst in Europe a period of stagnation prevailed and the learned treatises of the ancient world were lost or forgotten. Not until the twelfth century did ancient mathematical and scientific works start their slow passage back into Europe.

Spain, the north-western frontier of Moslem rule, became the threshold over which these treasures were reintroduced. When the translator Gerard of Cremona (1114–1187) journeyed to Toledo, in southern Spain, in search of Ptolemy's works, he found there a rich supply of Arabic versions of ancient Greek texts. By 1175 he had completed a Latin translation of Ptolemy's *Almagest*.

Soon, Latin editions of further classics, of Euclid, Aristotle and others, started to appear. Since Latin was, in effect, through Roman conquests, the common language of scholars throughout Europe, these works became marvelously accessible across national boundaries.

The fame of Ptolemy's masterpiece began to spread. Its reputation was greatly enhanced by the activities of King Alphonso X of Leon and Castile (1221–1284)—aptly nicknamed 'Alphonso the Wise'. He gathered together, in Toledo, a group of astronomers to produce a set of astronomical tables, based on the calculating methods of the *Almagest*. These were published in 1252 and considerably improved upon the accuracy of previous tables. They were in use for about three centuries, being the basis of almost all published astronomical almanacs until the mid-sixteenth century.

More than 200 years after their first appearance, one copy of the Alphonsine Tables found its way into the hands of a young student at the University of Cracow in Poland. In its margins he made notes on an alternative astronomical system which challenged the very foundations of Ptolemy's theory. The student was Nicolas Copernicus (1473–1543).

After his father died in 1483, the 10 year old Copernicus had been placed in the care of his uncle, Lucas Watzenrode, who later became Bishop of Ermland, in Prussia. Not surprisingly, his uncle guided him towards a clerical career and it was with this in mind that he arrived at the University of Cracow at the age of 18. Cracow was then the capital of a large commonwealth comprising Poland and Lithuania. Its imposing market square, the largest in Europe, showed that it was a thriving city, built on trade. The University,

Nicholas Copernicus

mirroring the cosmopolitan character of the city, attracted students from far afield. It was one of the first academic institutions in Northern Europe to be infused with the fresh spirit of enquiry brought into being by the re-discovery of the old Greek scientific texts. It was there that Copernicus started to display an interest in mathematics and astronomy. Although no record of his formal studies exists, it is clear that he began to devour the classic texts on astronomy. He would have read Aristotle's *On the Heavens*, which was still popular with his professors. As students of astronomy had done a

thousand years earlier, he would have ploughed painfully through the intricate reasoning of Ptolemy's *Almagest*.

For some time it seemed that Copernicus was destined to be a perpetual student. He travelled from Poland to the University of Bologna to study Law; then, after a brief return to Poland, back to Italy to study Medicine at Padua. He was awarded a doctorate in Canon Law in 1503 by the University of Ferrara in Italy, after which he resumed his medical studies in Padua for a couple of years. Only when he was in his early thirties did he return to settle in Poland. Through his uncle's influence he had secured a post as a canon at Frauenburg Cathedral, but for the time being he joined his uncle in Heilsberg as a medical adviser or physician.

Upon the death of his uncle in 1510, Copernicus moved to take up his position at Frauenburg (modern Frombork), a small coastal town overlooking the Gulf of Danzig (Gdansk) and the Baltic Sea. In this 'remote corner of the Earth', as he called it, he lived out the rest of his life. His duties included not only administering church affairs in Ermland, but also local government. Copernicus was no 'ivory tower' philosopher, but a man immersed in worldly affairs. Diplomacy in the midst of war, management of a currency in the midst of raging inflation, ministering to the sick, and many other practical problems, were the burdens which fell on his shoulders.

He had chosen for his residence one of the turrets on the defensive wall surrounding the cathedral. From the turret, there was a door opening out onto a platform, and from here, when Baltic mists permitted, observations of the night sky could be made. Mundane and clerical duties notwithstanding, he now had time and facilities to devote himself to his chief passion, Astronomy.

Though Copernicus was not an outstanding observer, his early mastery of the Alphonsine Tables showed him to be an earnest student of planetary movements. He was perturbed by the geometrical 'tricks' used by traditional astronomers in order to make their predictions of positions: '... some make use of homocentric circles only, others of eccentric circles and epicycles, by means of which however they do not fully attain what they seek...Moreover, they have not been able to discover or to infer the chief point of all, i.e., the form of the world and the certain commensurability of its parts.' [8] It was this

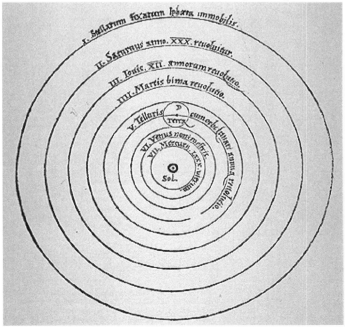

The Sun-centred universe of Copernicus

unease which lured him into the subversive ideas which he confided to the margins of his copy of the Alphonsine Tables.

Against Ptolemy, he argued that the daily rotation of the heavens was due to the Earth spinning on its own axis. 'The Earth together with its circumjacent elements [the atmosphere and seas] performs a complete rotation on its poles in a daily motion, whilst the unmoved firmament and highest heaven abide unchanged.'[9] But the greatest leap Copernicus made was that, in *his* theory, he made the Sun stand still and, in its stead, the Earth was made to move: '... the Sun, as if resting on a kingly throne, governs the family of stars [i.e. planets] which wheel around...'[10] He realised that, whether the Earth *or* the Sun was orbiting the other, the appearance of the Sun's motion in the sky would be the same. From this point of view, both theories were equally valid. But placing the Sun at the centre of the system, with all the planets orbiting about it, gave a much more satisfying explanation for a number of other phenomena.

The first of these was the long-standing problem of *retrograde motion*. Ptolemy had had to resort to the artificial device of the epicycle to ensure

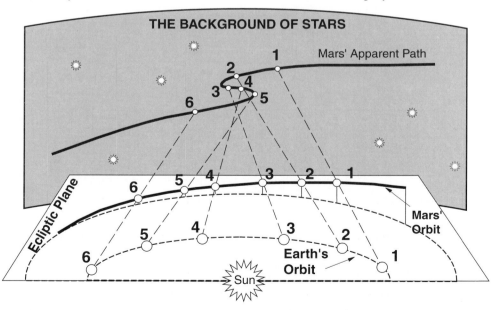

The retrograde motion of Mars, explained by the heliocentric theory of Copernicus

that Mars, for example, would occasionally appear to interrupt its west to east motion and retrace its path back towards the west, before once again resuming its easterly motion. The heliocentric, or 'sun-centred', theory of Copernicus, in contrast, immediately provided a simpler reason for the retrograde motion: when viewed against the background stars, Mars, as it was being overlapped on the inside, necessarily appeared to go backwards for a time, before continuing forward.

The heliocentric theory also enabled a much simpler interpretation of the maximum elongation of Venus and Mercury—that is, their maximum angular separation from the Sun. Because Venus and Mercury were in smaller orbits than the Earth about the Sun, they could never appear to stray a great distance to either side of the Sun, as viewed from the Earth.

Copernicus' theory not only accounted for this behaviour of the inner planets: it also permitted a startling deduction to be made from measurements of the maximum angle of separation from the Sun. Copernicus showed how this angle, measured when Venus is the 'Evening Star' and the 'Morning Star', can be used to deduce that the radius of Venus' orbit is approximately 72% of that of the Earth. In his calculations, perhaps to ensure that his theory rather than his data could be judged, Copernicus used the same raw data as Ptolemy—including some based on observations made by Theon, an Alexandrian mathematician, in 129 AD (see inset at the end of this chapter).

In the Copernican view of the Universe, certain other points in a planet's orbit, besides the maximum elongation, assume special importance. These all have to do with a planet's position relative to the Sun, as seen from the Earth. Of key significance for this story is the point known as *Conjunction*. A planet is said to be *in conjunction* with the Sun when it is in line with the Sun. For a planet which is nearer to the Sun than is the Earth, there are two points of conjunction: one when it is at the far side of the Sun—*Superior Conjunction*—and one when it is placed between the Earth and the Sun—*Inferior Conjunction*. Two planets—Mercury and Venus— fall into this category and, on account of their smaller orbits, are known as the *inferior* planets. The other planets, in orbits outside that of the Earth—*superior* planets—can only be in conjunction when they are at the far side of the Sun. When the Earth is interposed between the Sun and a superior planet, and all three lie in line, the planet is said to be in *Opposition*.

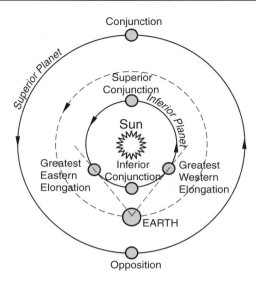

Aspects, or configurations, of the planets

Copernicus' ideas first saw the light of day in a short manuscript, known as the *Commentariolus* (or 'Little Commentary'), which was written for strictly limited circulation amongst friends. Private circulation, or not, the subversive ideas expressed in the *Commentariolus* were not easy to keep under wraps. They attracted a good deal of attention: not all of it welcome. Martin Luther (1483–1546), leader of the Protestant Reformation in Germany, described Copernicus as a fool for holding such opinions, in clear contradiction of the Bible. 'What appear to us as motions of the Sun arise not from its motion but from the motion of the Earth and our sphere, with which we revolve about the Sun like any other planet,' [11] asserted Copernicus in the opening pages. But, 'It was the Sun and not the Earth, which Joshua commanded to stand still', thundered Luther.

Not all church leaders were ready to condemn the new ideas however. Some were distinctly supportive. The Catholic Cardinal of Capua, Nicholas Schönberg, wrote to Copernicus in glowing terms: 'Some years ago word reached me concerning your proficiency, of which everybody constantly spoke. At that time I began to have a very high regard for you, and also to congratulate our contemporaries among whom you enjoyed such great prestige. For I learned that you had not merely mastered the discoveries of the ancient astronomers uncommonly well but had also formulated a new cosmology. In it you maintain that the earth moves; that the sun occupies the lowest, and thus the central, place in the universe; that the eighth heaven remains perpetually motionless and fixed; and that, together with the elements included in its sphere, the moon, situated between the heavens of Mars and Venus, revolves around the sun in the period of a year. I have also learned that you have written an exposition of this whole system of astronomy, and have computed the planetary motions and set them down in tables, to the greatest admiration of all. Therefore with the utmost earnestness I entreat you, most learned sir, unless I inconvenience you, to communicate this discovery of yours to scholars, and at the earliest moment to send me your writings on the sphere of the universe together with the tables and whatever else you have that is relevant to this subject. Moreover, I have instructed Theodoric of Regen to have everything copied in your quarters at my expense and dispatched to me. If you gratify my desire in this manner, you will see that you are dealing with a man who is zealous for your reputation and eager to do justice to so fine a talent. Farewell.' [12]

By the time Copernicus was approaching old age, Catholic Ermland, where he lived, was surrounded by Protestant territory. The religious strife of the Reformation was in full spate. In 1517 Martin Luther had provocatively nailed his ninety-five theses to the heavy oak door of Wittenberg church. The thudding of the nails into the door was as a fervent drumbeat summoning the various factions to arms. Throughout much of western Europe the clash of religious ideas was soon joined by the ferocious clash of weapons on the battlefield.

Ermlanders, by and large, viewed their Protestant neighbours with deep suspicion and loathing. The inhabitants of Wittenberg in particular were despised—as if, to a soul, they were ardent supporters of Luther. It was therefore a brave impulse which brought a young mathematics teacher from the Lutheran University of Wittenberg all the way to the doorstep of Copernicus in the Spring of 1539.

Georg Joachim Rheticus (1514–1574) had heard about the new system of astronomy espoused by Copernicus and was anxious to know more. He decided to make the trek to Frauenburg to acquire details first-hand. Rheticus did not need telling about the dangers. No one knew better than he the potentially disastrous consequences of religious temper and zealotry. His adoption of the name 'Rheticus' itself stemmed from a personal trauma of just such origin. He had been christened 'Iserin', but whilst he was still only fourteen years old his father was charged with sorcery and was beheaded. The young Iserin was not allowed to keep his father's surname. He adopted 'Rheticus' as his new surname to indicate that he came from a place in what had previously been the Roman province of Rhaetia.

Possibly to the disgust of some members of the Frauenburg brethren, the welcome Rheticus received from Copernicus was extremely cordial. Fortunately so, for this encounter was momentous for the development of astronomy. The more Rheticus learned about the new heliocentric theory, the more enthusiastic about it he became. He joined forces with Copernicus' friends Nicholas Schönberg and Tiedemann Giese, Bishop of Culm, in trying to convince the aging canon to publish the astronomical masterpiece upon which he was working. He managed to persuade Copernicus at least to allow publication of a short synopsis of the new ideas.

Subsequently, perhaps because no great fuss had followed this publication, the *Narratio Prima*, or First Account, Copernicus went ahead with plans for a more comprehensive exposition of his theory. Originally, Rheticus was to have overseen production, but when he accepted a post at the University of Leipzig in 1542, the work of putting the manuscript into a fit shape for publication was handed to a Lutheran theologian—Andreas Osiander. Without the consent of Copernicus, Osiander wrote an unsigned preface to the book, stating that its conclusions should not be regarded as necessarily true, but simply as hypothetical devices for predicting the movements of the planets. The explanations for the non-uniform motion of the planets were not to be taken literally: '... they are not put forward to convince anyone that they are true, but merely to provide a reliable basis for computation.' [13] Because the preface was unsigned, it appeared to be written by Copernicus himself. Friends were furious at this misrepresentation. Bishop Tiedemann Giese, knowing Copernicus' true conviction, even wrote to the publisher asking for a corrected version—minus Osiander's preface—to be printed, but to no avail.

In December 1542, Copernicus suffered a cerebral haemorrhage, which left him partially paralysed. The finished book, *De Revolutionibus Orbium Coelestium* (On the Revolutions of the Heavenly Spheres) is reputed to have reached him on his death-bed on 24th May 1543. There is no record to show whether he saw the misleading preface and, if so, the extent of his dismay.

Although *De Revolutionibus* did not exactly fall 'still-born from the press', neither did it immediately transform the thinking of the astronomical community. Nowadays, there is a tendency to ascribe to Copernicus the *proof* that the Earth moves around the Sun, whilst rotating on its own axis. This is not true. He did indeed propose such a system and this system produced results which were consistent with the known facts. In many ways, his heliocentric theory offered a much more elegant explanation for these facts. It was certainly acknowledged as the most masterly mathematical treatise on astronomy since the work of Ptolemy. Nevertheless, as to the conclusive proof, this was still missing. His contemporaries could still, with justice, remain sceptical.

Astronomical tables based on Copernican premises were produced by Erasmus Reinhold (1511–1553) in 1551. Called the *Prutenic Tables*, in honour of their sponsor—the Duke of Prussia—they were noticeably more accurate than their predecessor tables, but this was partly due to the calculating prowess of Reinhold, rather than being due to the different system upon which they were based.

For the time being, most astronomers preferred to stick with the tried and trusted model of Ptolemy.

HOW COPERNICUS SHOWED THE RELATIVE DISTANCES
OF VENUS AND THE EARTH FROM THE SUN

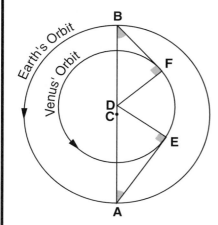

D is the centre of Venus' orbit

C is the centre of the Earth's orbit

At **F**, Venus is the 'Evening Star', seen from the Earth at **B**.

At **E**, Venus is the 'Morning Star', seen from the Earth at **A**.

Copernicus used the following observed maximum elongations (due to Theon):

Angle DBF = 47.3°; Angle DAE = 44.8°

Clearly, BD = DF / sin 47.3°
   and AD = DE / sin 44.8°
where DE = DF = the radius of Venus' orbit

The radius of the Earth's orbit, AC, is half of BD + AD.

Therefore, AC / DE = ½ [(1/sin 47.3°) + (1/sin 44.8°)]

Consequently, DE / AC = 0.7196, which is the value of Copernicus for the ratio of the radius of Venus' orbit to that of the Earth.

CHAPTER 4

THE SECRET OF THE PLANETS

Throughout the late Middle Ages, no serious astronomer would be without a copy of the Alphonsine Tables. These were the 'state of the art' means for applying the Ptolemaic system to the business of predicting planetary positions. To work out these positions from scratch, using Ptolemy's epicyclic theory, would be daunting even with modern calculating aids. By hand, it would have taken reams of calculations and many hours of labour. The Alphonsine Tables, by contrast, had pre-calculated most of the preliminary steps for establishing a planet's position. In this way, they made Ptolemy's theory much more 'user-friendly'. The positions predicted were sufficiently good to ensure that the tables sold thousands of copies. Nevertheless, when accurate timing of celestial events was important, severe shortcomings were sometimes evident.

No one was more acutely aware of these flaws than an enthusiastic young Danish astronomer called Tyge Brahe—soon to achieve renown as Tycho Brahe (1546–1601). He was disappointed to note that, when Jupiter overtook Saturn in 1563, the Alphonsine Tables were out by a full month in their prediction of the event.

Few people can have had such a bizarre start in life as the young Tycho. He was born into a noble family in 1546 in Skaane, which is now in Sweden. His father, Otto, was a government official and was eventually to become the Governor of Helsingborg Castle. Upon marrying, Otto had entered into an extraordinary agreement with his childless brother, Jörgen: namely, that the first son born of the marriage would be given to Jörgen, to bring up as his own. Jörgen was desperate to have a child upon whom he could lavish affection and bestow his wealth. In due course, Tycho was born. He was immediately claimed by Jörgen, but the parents promptly reneged on the deal. Parental instinct, which clearly had not been foreseen at the time of the bargain, got the better of them.

Although sorely offended, Jörgen at first made no attempt to force the issue. However, when, a year later, another child was born—a brother for Tycho—Jörgen asserted his 'right' by direct action. He *stole* his first-born nephew. Amazingly, after a time, the natural parents accepted the situation and, consequently, Tycho was brought up by his Uncle Jörgen.

At the age of 13, he was sent to the University of Copenhagen to study rhetoric and philosophy, to prepare him, as his uncle thought, for a career as a statesman. To no avail: an enduring interest in astronomy, instead, was awakened when he saw a partial eclipse of the Sun in 1560. What particularly impressed the youngster was the fact that such events could be predicted. It was 'something divine', he explained, 'that men could know the motions of the stars so accurately that they could long before foretell their places and relative positions'. [1]

His remaining time at Copenhagen was turned over to the study of Mathematics and Astronomy. By the age of 16 he was already an adept observer of the night sky.

In 1562, accompanied by a tutor, he went to the University of Leipzig to study law. The poor tutor, a young man named Anders Vedel, four years Tycho's senior, had a hard time keeping his youthful charge on task. Tycho's passion for astronomy was not to be

Tycho Brahe

diverted and he continued his study of it nightly, in secret, while Vedel was sleeping. He acquired a tiny globe—no bigger than a fist—which he secretly used to learn the constellations.

His quarrelsome personality made its mark early when he fought a duel at the age of 19, at a dance. As a result, he lost part of his nose and replaced it with one made of copper and silver.

An unexpected and dramatic event in the sky, however, was to grab the undivided attention of Tycho. By its stimulus, it would also propel him into a *career* of observing, which would lay the foundations for the modern understanding of how the planets move.

On 11th November 1572, 'in the evening, after sunset', he recounted, 'when, according to my habit, I was contemplating the stars in a clear sky, I noticed that a new and unusual star, surpassing the others in brilliancy, was shining almost directly above my head; and since I had, almost from boyhood, known all the stars of the heavens (there is no great difficulty in attaining that knowledge), it was quite evident to me that there had never before been any star in that

Tycho's New Star (I) in the constellation of Cassiopeia

place in the sky, even the smallest, to say nothing of a star so conspicuously bright as this. I was so astonished at this sight that I was not ashamed to doubt the trustworthiness of my own eyes.' [2]

Small wonder that Tycho questioned his own eyesight: this star was bright enough to be seen even in the daytime. It was in the constellation of Cassiopeia and can be deemed one of the most dramatic events in astronomical history. We now call such a star a *supernova*. Only six are known to have been witnessed before that of Tycho.

His brilliant new star gradually faded, changing colour along the way— first to yellow, then to red, until sixteen months later it could no longer be seen.

The new star, seen not only by scholars, but by millions of common folk, caused a great deal of discussion and consternation: after all, had not Aristotle told that the stars were eternal and unchanging? If so, was this new object *truly* a star? Some supposed that it was a portent of misfortunes to come. In this regard, it was held to be like comets, of which, Martin Luther had preached earlier in the century, 'God creates not one that does not foretoken a sure calamity.' [3] Others, such as Beza, friend of the religious leader Calvin, speculated that it was a second Star of Bethlehem, heralding a second coming of Christ on Earth. Few people were left unstirred. Even the sober-minded Tycho deemed it 'a miracle indeed, either the greatest of all that have occurred in the whole range of nature since the beginning of the world, or one certainly that is to be classed with those attested by the Holy Oracles, the staying of the Sun in its course in answer to the prayers of Joshua, and the darkening of the Sun's face at the time of the Crucifixion.' [4]

Tycho steadfastly observed the star throughout its brief life. He repeatedly took measurements of its angular distance from neighbouring stars. In particular he took measurements when it was high in the sky and compared these with ones taken when it was low. He discovered no discernible parallax. In other words, its relative position did not appear displaced when, thanks to the Earth's rotation, it was viewed from a different vantage point. If the new star had been at the same distance as the Moon there should have been an apparent shift of one degree in its position relative to the other stars. It was clearly, Tycho thought, as distant as the background of fixed stars. A serious blow was thus delivered to the authority of Aristotle's astronomy, in which the starry firmament was supposed to be unchanging.

Tycho published his findings in a book in 1573. It was typical of the times that he delayed publishing the book, *De Nova Stella (On the New Star)*, because it was considered undignified for a nobleman to write books! Typifying the half-way house between old and new astronomy, which Tycho occupied, parts of the book were devoted to astrology and to predictions of the events which were foreshadowed by the appearance of the star.

The apparition of the new star spurred him to question further the accepted view of the universe. Aristotle had said that transient phenomena, like comets, must be atmospheric in origin, because the crystalline heavenly spheres were immutable. Clearly this had been wrong as far as the new star was concerned. Perhaps it was also wrong for comets. Tycho resolved to subject, one day, a comet to the same test—parallax measurement—as he had used for the new star.

Nature quickly obliged. In 1577 a brilliant comet appeared in the sky. Its tail was quite something—22° long: the length of more than forty full moons, laid side-by-side. When Tycho duly made his observations, he found no perceptible parallax. He deduced that the comet was therefore up among the planets and stars: not in the atmosphere. Not only was the comet as distant as the supposed crystalline spheres: as time went on, it was moving between them, without hindrance. The conclusion was plain—the spheres did not exist.

The remainder of Tycho Brahe's life was devoted to meticulous astronomical observation and measurement. With the aid of royal patronage— as well as his own resources—he built magnificent observatories: first Uraniborg (the Castle of the Heavens) on the island of Hven, in the Danish Sound, and later at the Castle of Benatky on the outskirts of Prague.

Within these observatories Tycho accumulated a veritable mountain of astronomical data. Using improved measuring instruments, to his own design—large quadrants, sextants and armillas—he and his assistants produced measurements of unprecedented accuracy. Over a period of 24 years the positions of the stars and the movements of the planets amongst them were painstakingly recorded. Unlike most of his predecessors, Tycho understood that if one were to understand the subtle movements of the celestial bodies, then frequent observation of each body was a necessity. Even the great Copernicus had only included a few observations in his book. Tycho, in contrast, had recorded thousands of positions for each body. What is more, he appreciated that even the best of instruments has imperfections and he devised observing techniques which tended to eliminate many of the resulting errors.

Whilst Tycho was making his historic measurements of the Great Comet of 1577, the majestic sight of the comet was leaving an indelible mark on the minds of all who saw it. Included among these was a five year old child, who would, in adulthood, engage in a brief collaboration with Tycho, which would guarantee immortality for both their names. On a slope overlooking his home town in southern Germany, Johannes Kepler (1571–1630) stood gazing at the comet with his mother, Katharina. Possibly, she was unaware how vividly the sight would live on in her son's imagination. Without a doubt, she could not have known how the interest, thereby aroused, would cause him, in adult life, to revolutionise human understanding of the heavens.

Johannes was born on 27th December 1571, at Weil der Stadt, in Germany. His childhood was scarred by ill-health. At the age of four he suffered a severe attack of smallpox, which left him with damaged eyesight, crippled hands and a permanently weakened constitution. Maybe this was a blessing in disguise, for it led to him being guided towards a career in the Church, rather than into agricultural labour, which might otherwise have been his lot. He was sent at 13 to a monastic school at Adelberg and eventually to study philosophy at the University of Tübingen.

Johannes Kepler

Whilst still a student at Tübingen, Kepler became an ardent supporter of Copernicus' sun-centred theory of the solar system. He had heard a lecture on it by Michael Maestlin (1550–1631), the Professor of Mathematics. Maestlin himself was not a committed Copernican, but had put the case sympathetically. Possibly a bold act in itself: these were dangerous times for people with unorthodox ideas. Giordano Bruno (c.1548–1600), an enthusiastic proponent of the Copernican theory, having spoken repeatedly on the theme throughout Europe, was soon to be burned as a heretic in Rome.

In 1594 Kepler landed a post teaching maths at the high school of Graz. It didn't turn out to be the most demanding of jobs: during the first year, very few students attended his lectures, and during the second year, there were none! At least, he had sufficient leisure time to immerse himself in the deepening of his astronomical knowledge. His attention was captured above all by the relative distances of the known planets from the Sun.

During the course of his speculations he developed a remarkable explanation for the relative distances. He used as his starting point, Copernicus' assumption that the five known planets were in circular orbits around the Sun. Kepler claimed that the spacing of these orbits, in relative terms, was equivalent to the spacing of a series of concentric spheres, held apart by polyhedra tightly jammed into the gap between them. The hollow spheres and polyhedra were stacked in alternating fashion, one within the other, like Russian dolls. Each polyhedron had to be regular and had to have a number of sides from the

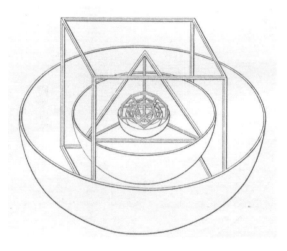

Kepler's spheres and polyhedra

sequence 8, 20, 12, 4 and 6 as one worked outwards from the Sun. That is, the polyhedron between the Sun and Mercury would have 8 sides—a perfect octahedron—and the one between Jupiter and Saturn would have 6 sides— a perfect cube. Kepler seems to have had semi-mystical, or astrological, reasons for considering that this numerical relationship was significant.

In 1596 he published his conclusions in a work called *The Cosmographic Mystery*. He sent copies to several noted astronomers, including Tycho Brahe. Tycho had quit Denmark, after losing the patronage of the royal court, and was now living near Hamburg, in Germany. He received it in 1598, but was not convinced. This was hardly surprising as, apart from any other issue, Tycho didn't even support the heliocentric premise of the book. A system which required the Earth to move, he could never accept. 'That heavy mass of the Earth, so ill-disposed towards motion, cannot be displaced and agitated in this way, without conflicting with the principles of physics. The authority of the Holy Scriptures opposes it…' [5], he had written in 1582. His opinion had not wavered by the time he received the unsolicited tome from Kepler. Nevertheless, Tycho could not help but recognise that its author had a signal knowledge of astronomy and was clearly a superb manipulator of complex data. He was intrigued and responded by inviting Kepler to visit him. The distance from Graz, however, made it impossible for a young man of Kepler's modest means to take up the invitation.

By fortuitous circumstance, it then happened that Tycho Brahe, accepted the post of Imperial Mathematician in the court of Rudolf II, the Habsburg emperor. After a few months in his new post, he wrote a cordial letter to Kepler. In it he spoke, diplomatically, of his high regard for the *Cosmographic Mystery*, but also explained his misgivings about it. More importantly, for Kepler, he promised to 'impart to you many of my observations, if you visit me one day as you promise. It will be less difficult for you than heretofore, because I have fixed upon a fresh site for Urania in Bohemia not far from you, and I am living in the Imperial castle of Benatky, five leagues from Prague.' [6]

The letter was unnecessary: Kepler had already set off to Benatky! He later wrote: 'I…ascribe it to divine arrangement that [Tycho] came to Bohemia.' [7] The *Cosmographic Mystery*, for all that it was completely mistaken, had secured a meeting which was to be pivotal for the progress of astronomy and science.

Before meeting Tycho, Kepler had firmly set his sights on the wealth of data in the Dane's possession. 'My opinion of Tycho is this:', wrote Kepler a year earlier, 'he is superlatively rich, but he knows not how to make proper use of it as is the case with most rich people. Therefore, one must try to wrest his riches from him, to get from him by begging the decision to publish all his observations without reservation.' [8]

On arrival, Kepler found Benatky Castle to be an insufferably loud and bustling place. Craftsmen swarmed everywhere, as Tycho insisted on structural alterations to bring the castle into line with his wishes. He had once boasted that the Danish King had spent more than a ton of Gold on the splendid observatory at Uraniborg. Maybe his new patron felt a tinge of unease on hearing about the pace of work at Benatky!

Meal times involved the whole household: Tycho's family—two sons and four daughters—co-workers and students, all gathered together to eat and chatter, sometimes interminably. Kepler, never a gregarious man, must have found the experience quite wearing.

One of the co-workers was Christian Severinus Longomontanus. He had lived with Tycho at Uraniborg for eight years and was still with 'the Master' when Kepler arrived at Benatky in February 1600. Because an opposition of Mars was at hand, he had recently been given the task of sifting through the observations of Mars, to try working out a theory for its motions, which would match the facts. Given the apparently irregular motion of Mars—its retrograde motion and sharp changes in latitude—this was no easy task. Longomontanus failed to make any meaningful headway, and, at his request, he moved onto the question of the Moon's motion, leaving Kepler to be assigned the work on Mars. 'Had Christian been treating a different planet,' related Kepler, 'I would have started on it as well. I therefore once again think it to have happened by divine arrangement, that I arrived at the same time in which he was intent upon Mars, whose motions provide the only possible access to the hidden secrets of astronomy, without which we would remain forever ignorant of those secrets.' [9]

But, collaboration with Tycho was a frustrating experience. It was no easy matter to 'wrest his riches from him.' Kepler complained bitterly in private correspondence that Tycho gave him 'no opportunity to share in his experiences. He would only, in the course of a meal, and in between conversing about other matters mention, as if in passing, today the figure for the apogee of one planet, tomorrow the nodes of another.' [10] Eventually however, seeing the boldness and ingenuity of Kepler's handling of the information, Tycho relaxed his grip on the invaluable records of his observations. The two often quarrelled, but without Kepler's arrival it is probable that Tycho Brahe's lifework would have gone unexploited. Tycho himself had but a little time left. His health was failing and at the end of October 1601 he fell ill. Sensing that the end was near, he several times implored his friends: 'Let me not seem to have lived in vain.' [11] Within eleven days he was dead.

Shortly after the death of Tycho Brahe, Kepler was appointed to succeed him as the Imperial Mathematician in the court of Rudolf II. Tycho's instruments however did not pass to him, nor at first did the records of his predecessor's observations. It took a protracted dispute with one of Tycho's heirs before the records entered Kepler's hands.

There followed a long period of gruelling work for Kepler as he tested one hypothesis after another, with regard to the motion of Mars, against the observations which he had inherited. Each hypothesis had to try to account for the position of Mars in the sky, as seen from a moving Earth. Thus, the hypothesis had to embody a theory for the motion of the Earth, as well as one for Mars itself.

Indefatigably, he laboured over labyrinthine calculations to compute the effect of concentric circular orbits, eccentric circles, epicycles upon circles, and so on. All to no avail. Sometimes, the positions predicted by a hypothesis would come close to the recorded observations, but still with unexplained disparities.

Kepler resisted the temptation to fudge the figures. Scrupulous honesty permeated his processing of the data. Above all, he refused to blame the disparities on inaccurate observation by Tycho. And yet, it would have been easy to ignore the 'lack of fit' between theory and observation: one of his geometrical schemes produced results which were never more than 8 arc-minutes from the observed positions of Mars. Bearing in mind that the unaided eye can scarcely distinguish between two stars separated by an angle of 4 arc-minutes, any lesser person would have been readily satisfied. Kepler explained the matter thus: 'Since the divine benevolence has vouchsafed us Tycho Brahe, a most diligent observer, from whose observations the 8 minute error in this … calculation is shown, it is fitting that we with thankful mind both acknowledge and honour this benefit of God…For if I had thought I could ignore eight minutes of longitude…I would already have made enough of a correction in the hypothesis found in chapter 16. Now, because they could not have been ignored, these eight minutes alone will have led the way to the reformation of all of astronomy.' [12]

Kepler abandoned the circular hypothesis and moved on to consider oval shaped orbits. Eventually, to his great joy, he found that the extremely simple oval curve known as the ellipse provided a near perfect fit. 'It was as if I were awakened from sleep to see a new light' [13], he declared. If the Sun was regarded as being at one focus of the ellipse, Tycho's observations at last started to make sense.

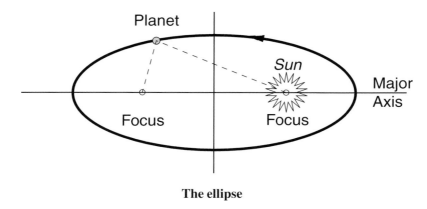

The ellipse

The ellipse had been familiar to geometers since antiquity. It is any closed curve in which, for every point on the curve, the sum of that point's distances from two fixed points is constant. Each of the fixed points is called a *focus*. The further the focus is from the centre of an ellipse, then the more elongated or cigar-shaped the ellipse is: its eccentricity increases.

After deducing the shape of the orbit of Mars, Kepler then went on to derive a set of rules describing its rate of motion. Clearly, if Mars moves along an elliptical path, its distance from the Sun must vary with time. Kepler found that Mars moved faster when it was near to the Sun and slowed down as it reached the furthest point from the Sun. He found moreover, through painstaking calculation, that the area swept out by an imaginary line joining the planet to the Sun is always proportional to the time of travel.

His results were ready for publication in 1605, but due to cash problems in the Imperial Treasury, they did not see the light of day until 1609. Eight years after the death of Tycho, Kepler's book, *New Astronomy,* was the first fruit of the Danish astronomer's legacy. The book was not the world's most riveting read: just the opposite. It was extremely long and, within its pages, Kepler insisted on relating the entire story of his travails: all the blind alleys and false hypotheses. Indeed, he had apparently written 58 chapters of the book, in their more or less final version, before discovering that the motion of Mars was an ellipse! In the Preface he wrote: 'Here it is a question not only of leading the reader to an understanding of the subject matter in the easiest way, but also, chiefly, of the arguments, meanderings, or even chance occurrences by which I the author first came upon that understanding. Thus, in telling of Christopher Columbus, Magellan, and of the Portuguese, we do not simply ignore the errors by which the first opened up America, the second, the China Sea, and the last, the coast of Africa; rather, we would not wish them omitted, which would indeed be to deprive ourselves of an enormous pleasure in reading. So likewise, I would not have it ascribed to me as a fault that with the same concern for the reader I have followed this same course in the present work.' [14]

No wonder students didn't attend his lectures!

The monumental scale of the new book did not mark an end to Kepler's labours. Doggedly, he continued the search for a general theory of planetary motion, acutely aware of the duty which went with the possession of Tycho's archives. There was no time to spare for all the trappings which no doubt could have accompanied his station: 'High position and great honours do not exist for me...', he wrote to Maestlin, 'I conduct myself as though I did not serve the Emperor, but the whole of mankind, as well as posterity. With this assurance, I have kept a secret pride in despising all honours and positions, and, if necessary, even those who confer them. The only honour for me is to have been entrusted by Divine Providence with the observations of Tycho Brahe.' [15]

The steadfastness of Kepler, grappling with the problems of planetary motion, is all the more remarkable when considered against the backdrop of misfortune afflicting his personal life.

In the January of 1611, his three children caught smallpox and in February, as a result, his treasured six-year old son, Frederick, died. As Frederick lay dying, a war, in which Emperor Rudolf, Kepler's sponsor, was deposed, brought Austrian troops onto the streets of Prague. Kepler's position became untenable. He attempted to move back to his homeland, Württemberg, but this was blocked by the authorities there, for religious reasons.

He finally decided to move to Linz, partly for the sake of his wife, Barbara. Then a further tragedy struck. Before the move took place, Barbara succumbed to one of the contagious diseases introduced to Prague by the war. Disconsolately, Kepler described her passing: 'Stunned by the deeds of horror of the soldiers and the sight of the bloody fighting in the city, consumed by despair of a better future and by the unquenched yearning for her darling lost son, to bring an end to her troubles she was infected by the Hungarian spotted typhus, her mercy taking revenge on her, since she would not be kept from visiting the sick. In melancholy despondency, the saddest frame of mind under the sun, she finally expired.' [16]

Before long, after settling down to his new job as District Mathematician in Linz, Kepler re-married. His new wife, Susanna, bore six children, but, between 1617 and 1623, three of them became ill and died.

A more sinister distraction tormented him between 1615 and 1620. Back in Württemberg, his mother, Katharina, was accused of being a witch. In due course, she was put on trial for her life. These were unsafe times. In nearby Weil der Stadt alone, during the years 1615–1629, thirty-eight 'witches', convicted on the basis of tittle-tattle and hysterical superstition, were executed in a most gruesome fashion. Kepler travelled to Württemberg to conduct the defence, and submitted a 128-page deposition, answering the case against his mother. With obvious irritation, the scribe at the trial recorded that 'the prisoner appears, alas, with the support of her gentleman son, Johannes Kepler, the mathematician.' [17] Alas, indeed, for the persecutors, because, against the odds, the defence succeeded and Frau Kepler was released. Even so, she did not dare return to her home town, for fear of being beaten to death by her former neighbours. Seven months later, lonely and severely weakened by her traumatic ordeal, she passed away. 'Thus,' in the words of Kepler's biographer, Max Caspar, 'Frau Katharina Kepler, who had given the intellectual world such a wonderfully radiant luminary, her son Johannes, ended her own life in obscurity.' [18]

Throughout all these vicissitudes, Kepler laboured on with his considera-
tion of the movements of the planets. Many years of study were to follow
before he could prove that what applied to Mars also applied to the other
planets. The main conclusions of his earlier work—*New Astronomy*—then
became Kepler's first two Laws of Planetary Motion:-

1   *All planets move in ellipses, the Sun being at one focus*, and,
2   *The straight line joining a planet to the Sun sweeps out equal areas in
     equal intervals of time.*

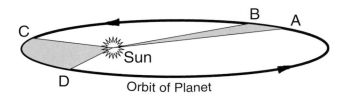

**Kepler's Second Law: If the time for a planet to travel from A to
B is the same as from C to D, then both areas swept out are equal**

In 1619 he published *Harmonies of the World*, containing another key
discovery, which later became known as his Third Law. Still unable to let go
of his semi-mystical fascination with numerical ratios occurring in the
planetary orbits, Kepler had explored the relative distances of the planets
from the Sun and compared these with the times taken by each planet to
complete one orbit. With his *Cosmographic Mystery* he had struck a worthless
seam of enquiry, but now he struck gold. He found that *the squares of the
times of revolution of any two planets about the Sun are proportional to the
cubes of their mean distances from the Sun.* This was no mere oddity—a
meaningless coincidence: what Kepler had discovered was the astronomical
equivalent of the Holy Grail—the key to the size of the Solar System.

Kepler did not know the *actual* distances of the planets from the Sun. His
Third Law could be applied simply on the basis of relative distances. If
Earth-years are used as the unit of time and the Earth-Sun distance (the
'astronomical unit') as the unit of distance, everything falls neatly into place.

The ratio of the 'orbital period squared' to the 'mean distance cubed' is a constant value whichever the planet. Thus, if the orbital period of the Earth is one year and we say that the mean distance of the Earth from the Sun is one Astronomical Unit, then the all-important ratio has a numerical value of *one*: taking the Earth, for example, the ratio is one squared, divided by one cubed.

Provided that we use the same units of measurement—Earth-years and Astronomical Units—Kepler's Third Law means that the ratio must be *one* for every other planet.

	Mercury	Venus	Earth	Mars	Jupiter	Saturn
Square of Periodic Time	0.058	0.378	1	3.54	140.7	867.7
Cube of Mean Distance	0.058	0.378	1	3.54	140.8	867.9

The implication of this was that if astronomers could discover the *actual* distance of any planet—for example, the Earth—from the Sun, then, knowing the period times, they would be immediately enabled to calculate the distance of every other planet.

In *Harmonies of the World*, Kepler reflected upon his achievement: 'What I prophesied two-and-twenty years ago, as soon as I discovered the five solids among the heavenly orbits...that for which I joined Tycho Brahe, for which I settled in Prague, for which I devoted the best part of my life to astronomical contemplations, at length I have brought to light and recognised its truth beyond my most sanguine expectations...The die is cast, and I write this book. Whether it will be read by my contemporaries or by posterity is not important. If God himself has waited six thousand years for someone to contemplate his works, my book can wait for a hundred.' [19]

Kepler's discovery of the laws of planetary motion enabled him to complete the task originally envisioned by Tycho Brahe: the production of comprehensive astronomical tables, enabling astronomers, navigators and cartographers to predict accurately the position of the planets at any time. These tables, named the *Rudolphine Tables*, in honour of the long dead Emperor, were published by Kepler at his own expense in 1627. They represented his crowning glory. One thousand copies were printed—an unprecedented figure for a scientific book in those days. More importantly, the accuracy of the tables was unprecedented in the history of astronomy.

Three years later Johannes Kepler was dead.

In many senses, the way in which he and his predecessors practised astronomy was also dead. Not their meticulous striving for accuracy, nor their rigorous demand that theory must match observation—these would always be indispensable virtues—but their total reliance on the naked-eye. As Kepler was going to print with his *New Astronomy* in 1609, in southern Europe an entirely new instrument was being turned to the skies.

That instrument was destined to throw the horizon of astronomy out to unimagined distances. It was wielded by Galileo Galilei (1564–1642), already a celebrated mathematician and experimenter, in Padua, Italy.

CHAPTER 5

'THE SHAPES OF CYNTHIA'

In Galileo, the University of Padua not only had a successful teacher of mathematics and astronomy, it also had an avid designer of scientific instruments. For the manufacture of his designs, Galileo adapted one room of his house as a shop and hired a craftsman to work there. At least one of his designs, a proportional compass, was very profitable.

In the June or July of 1609 his attention turned to a new instrument which had been invented in Holland. 'A report reached my ears', he wrote, 'that a certain Dutchman had constructed a spyglass by means of which visible objects, though very distant from the eye of the observer, were distinctly seen as if nearby. Of this truly remarkable effect several experiences were related, to which some persons gave credence while others denied them. A few days later the report was confirmed to me in a letter from a noble Frenchman at Paris, Jacques Badovere, which caused me to apply myself wholeheartedly to inquire into the means by which I might arrive at the invention of a similar instrument. This I did shortly afterwards, my basis being the theory of refraction. First I prepared a tube of lead, at the ends of which I fitted two glass lenses, both plane on one side while on the other side one was spherically convex and the other concave. Then placing my eye near the concave lens I perceived objects satisfactorily large and near, for they appeared three times closer and nine times larger than when seen with the naked eye alone. Next I constructed another one, more accurate, which represented objects as enlarged more than sixty times. Finally, sparing neither labour nor expense, I succeeded in constructing for myself so excellent an instrument that objects seen by means of it appeared nearly one thousand times larger and over thirty times closer than when regarded with our natural vision'. [1]

Soon Galileo turned his spyglass—the term *telescope* was not coined until 1611—to the night sky. He was met by an awe-inspiring sight: a host of stars 'in numbers ten times exceeding the old and familiar stars' and the moon, magnified 'so that its diameter appears almost thirty times larger ... than when viewed with the naked eye'. [2] He could see that the Moon, far from being the perfect, smooth sphere, previously assumed, was a world of mountains, valleys and craters.

Galileo Galilei

He was not content to merely gaze in wonder at the stars. He wanted to measure their disposition. 'I began to seek (and eventually found)', he wrote, 'a method by which I might measure their distances apart.' [3]

Galileo then turned his attention to the five known planets and it was here that his most momentous findings were to occur. Through the telescope the planets appeared as discs rather than merely as points of light like the stars. The planets clearly had a finite size and different apparent diameters.

Early in the evening of 7th January 1610, as he was looking at Jupiter through his telescope, he noticed 'that beside the planet there were three starlets, small indeed, but very bright. Though I believed them to be among the host of fixed stars, they aroused my curiosity somewhat by appearing to lie in an exact straight line parallel to the ecliptic, and by their being more splendid than others of their size.' [4] He made a note of their arrangements: two stars on the eastern side and one to the west. The next evening all three starlets were to the west of Jupiter. Some days later he noticed that there were four starlets, again the pattern having changed.

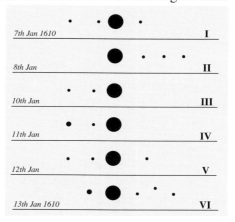

7th Jan 1610   I

8th Jan   II

10th Jan   III

11th Jan   IV

12th Jan   V

13th Jan 1610   VI

Captivated, Galileo kept up his observations for the best part of two months. By the middle of January he felt convinced that the only explanation for the changing pattern was that the four starlets— moons or satellites, as we would call them—were 'wandering about Jupiter as do Venus and Mercury about the Sun'. [5] He began to record

Galileo's record of Jupiter and its moons on successive nights

each night the exact position of Jupiter relative to the fixed stars and the distance of each of the starlets from Jupiter in minutes of arc.

The received wisdom at the time was that all celestial bodies are in orbit about the Earth, yet here was direct evidence that other centres of orbital motion could exist. These observations lent weight to the Copernican view of the solar system, at least insofar as they demolished the *dogma* that the Earth must *necessarily* be the centre of all motion. A fascinating mirror image of that dogma was the discomfort of many Copernicans with the fact that the system of Copernicus had all the planets moving around the Sun, but the Moon moving about the Earth. This seemed quite incongruous in an age which had not yet divested itself of the systems of concentric spheres and perfect uniformity so dear to ancient philosophers.

The existence of Jupiter's star-like moons now provided 'a fine and elegant argument', according to Galileo, 'for quieting the doubts of those who, while accepting with tranquil mind the revolutions of the planets about the Sun in the Copernican system, are mightily disturbed to have the Moon alone revolve about the Earth and accompany it in an annual rotation about the Sun. Some have believed that this structure of the universe should be rejected as impossible. But now we have not just one planet rotating about another while both run through a great orbit around the Sun; our own eyes show us four stars which wander around Jupiter as does the Moon around the Earth, while all together trace a grand revolution about the Sun in the space of twelve years.' [6]

Galileo quickly went into print with an account of his discoveries. Five hundred copies of his book, *The Starry Messenger* (*Siderius Nuncius*) were published in 1610. They sold out immediately and, with orders coming in from all over Europe, another edition was printed in the same year. News of his amazing discoveries spread rapidly, far beyond Italy, and the demand for telescopes soared.

Not everyone accepted the truth of Galileo's reports. The eminent Jesuit astronomer, Father Christopher Clavius (1537–1612), chief mathematician at the Roman College, was reported as saying that in order to see Galileo's starlets one would first have to put them in the telescope! It was a particular source of satisfaction for Galileo therefore, when he learned towards the end of 1610 that Father Clavius and his colleagues had seen and confirmed the satellites of Jupiter (though not necessarily Galileo's conclusions). Clavius' younger collaborator, Father Grienberger wrote to Galileo in January 1611: 'Things so hard to believe as what you assert neither can nor should be believed lightly; I know how difficult it is to dismiss opinions sustained for many centuries by the authority of so many scholars. And surely, if I had not seen, so far as the instruments allowed, these wonders with my own eyes…I do not know whether I would have consented to your arguments.' [7]

While the world was in thrall to the new sights in the sky, Galileo continued his observing. The rush to publish *The Starry Messenger* meant that he had not had chance to view Mars, Saturn and Venus in favourable conditions. In October he started a systematic watch on Venus. What he saw over the next few months provided powerful evidence for the Copernican system, as opposed to that of Ptolemy.

In the system of Ptolemy, the Sun orbits around the Earth and so does Venus. It was well known however, even to the casual observer, that Venus is never to be found more than about 47° to the east or west of the Sun. When to the east, Venus could be seen, shortly after sunset, as the bright, so-called *'Evening Star'*; when to the west of the Sun, it could be seen in the hours before dawn, as the *'Morning Star'*. To explain this apparent movement to either side of the Sun, Ptolemy proposed that Venus travelled along an epicycle—a circular motion, superimposed upon its orbit about the Earth. The rate at which this epicycle moved around the Earth was supposed to exactly match the motion of the Sun, thus explaining their enduring companionship in the heavens.

It seems likely that Galileo had seen Venus as a small, but brilliant, disc in the autumn of 1610. He knew that, if Venus shone by reflecting the light of the Sun, it could never be seen as a full, circular disc in Ptolemy's scheme of things (see illustration above), yet here it was *as a disc*. A disc was certainly to be expected from the Copernican model, when the planet was at superior conjunction—i.e. at the far side of the Sun. The only possibilities were that either, Ptolemy was wrong, or Venus shone, not by reflection of sunlight, but with light of its own.

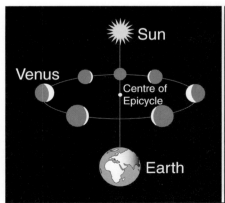 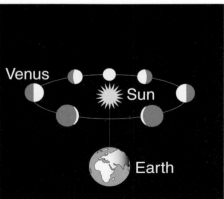

Phases of Venus in Ptolemy's system	**Phases of Venus in Copernicus' system**

By late November, Venus had not only grown in size when viewed through his telescope, but had started to display a distinct half-moon shape. With his excitement mounting, but not yet in a position to produce a full report, Galileo sent a mysterious anagram to Giuliano de' Medici, ambassador in Prague. The anagram was a technique beloved of seventeenth century scientists for establishing priority of discovery. Galileo had cause to believe that others were gazing at Venus, with precisely the same reasons in mind.

Not until New Year's Day in 1611 did Galileo decipher the anagram for its recipient. Rearranged, it read: *'Cynthiae figuras aemulatur mater amorum'*, or 'The mother of loves imitates the shapes of Cynthia'. In other words, Venus imitates the phases of our Moon (Cynthia). By this time Venus had developed a very clear crescent shape. It was beyond dispute that Venus was indeed shining with the reflected light of the Sun and its full set of phases had comprehensively demolished the Ptolemaic account of its motion.

The phases of Venus seen by Galileo

Christopher Clavius, the Jesuit, quickly realised that Ptolemy's view of the universe had been rendered untenable. In his commentary on the *Sphere* by the thirteenth century writer, Sacrobosco, Clavius wrote, possibly with a tinge of regret in his tone: 'I do not want to hide from the reader that not long ago a certain instrument was brought from Belgium. It has the form of a long tube in the bases of which are set two glasses, or rather lenses, by which objects far away from us appear very much closer...than the things themselves are. This instrument shows many more stars in the firmament than can be seen in any way without it...Consult the reliable little book by Galileo Galilei, printed at Venice in 1610 and called Siderius Nuncius, which describes various observations of the stars first made by him.

'Far from the least important of things seen with this instrument is that Venus receives its light from the Sun as does the Moon, so that sometimes it appears to be more like a crescent, sometimes less, according to its distance from the Sun. At Rome I have observed this, in the presence of others, more than once…Jupiter has four roving stars, which vary their places in a remarkable way both among themselves and with respect to Jupiter—as Galileo Galilei carefully and accurately describes.

'Since things are thus, astronomers ought to consider how the celestial orbs may be arranged in order to save these phenomena [i.e. explain the appearances].' [8]

Clavius was no stranger to the task of salvaging traditions which had fallen out of step with astronomical reality. It was he who persuaded Pope Gregory XIII (1502–1585) that the calendar was running 10 days behind time and was in dire need of reform. The calendar which was in use had been introduced by Julius Caesar in the first century BC. It dictated that a year would normally have 365 days, but an extra day would be added to February every fourth year. In this way, the year, on average, would have 365¼ days. Compared with the length of the solar year—the year

Father Christopher Clavius

which governed the seasons—this was almost exactly right. But not quite! The length of the solar year was about 11 minutes less than this. Not a significant amount, one might think. Nevertheless, over the course of 128 years, an accumulated error of one whole day resulted.

Holy Days in general, and Easter in particular, were fixed by reference to lunar and solar cycles. By the sixteenth century, the drift of the calendar was not only making the Spring Equinox occur at the wrong time, it was also making Holy Days extremely difficult to fix.

Pope Gregory was convinced and in 1582 introduced the new calendar which bears his name and is still in use today. The Gregorian calendar, by dropping 11 days in the first year, immediately brought things back into step. It also included a provision that century years would only be leap years—having an extra day—when divisible by 400. This ensured that the calendar *stayed* in step. Catholic countries adopted the changes fairly readily, but Protestant countries had to be dragged to them kicking and screaming. The English calendar, for example, was not changed until one hundred and seventy years later, in 1752. In that year, September had only 19 days.

In 1612, Clavius died and the task of rearranging the Catholic Church's view of the celestial orbs, to tie in with Galileo's observations, fell to his younger colleagues.

Biblical scriptures, taken literally, presented a serious stumbling block, since they appeared to rule out any system in which the Earth moved. 'O Lord my God', runs Psalm 104, '…who laid the foundations of the earth, that it should not be removed for ever.' Many Catholic astronomers were familiar with the Copernican theory and even preferred its tables as a means of calculating planetary positions, but they viewed it simply as a convenient mathematical device: not as a representation of reality.

In an open letter to the Grand Duchess Christina in 1615, Galileo took the bull by the horns. He boldly proclaimed the heliocentric theory of Copernicus and tried to explain why it was not at odds with any right-thinking interpretation of the Bible. He admitted that 'in many places in the Bible one may read that the Sun moves and the Earth stands still.' Nevertheless, he went on, it is 'prudent to affirm that the Holy Bible can never speak untruth—whenever its true meaning is understood. But I believe nobody will deny that it is often very abstruse, and may say things which are quite different from what its bare words signify.' He argued that the Bible was full of propositions uttered by the Holy Spirit and 'set down in that manner by the sacred scribes in order to accommodate them to the capacities of the common people, who are rude and unlearned.' [9] In summary, he repeated the now famous epigram: 'the intention of the Holy Spirit is to teach us how one goes to heaven, not how heaven goes.' [10]

In response to Galileo's letter, the leading theologian, Cardinal Bellarmino, insisted that Copernican ideas were all very well as long as they did not purport to be the literal truth: 'to say that assuming the Earth moves and the Sun stands still saves all the appearances better than eccentrics and epicycles is to speak well. This has no danger in it, and it suffices for mathematicians.

But to wish to affirm that the Sun is really fixed in the centre of the heavens and that the Earth is situated in the third sphere and revolves very swiftly around the Sun is a very dangerous thing, not only by irritating all the theologians and scholastic philosophers, but also by injuring our holy faith and making the sacred Scripture false.' [11]

The heightened profile of the controversy prompted church officials to publicly condemn the teaching of Copernicus and to place his book, *De Revolutionibus*, on the Index of Prohibited Books—from which it would not be removed until 1835.

Jesuit astronomers meanwhile retreated from the planetary system of Ptolemy and sought refuge in a hybrid system devised by Tycho Brahe. In Brahe's system the Earth was still stationary at the centre of the universe, but Mercury and Venus orbited the Sun, and the Sun orbited the Earth.

The Church sought to persuade Galileo to tone down his speeches and writings and for a number of years it seemed that this strategy had been successful. Ironically, the issue was re-opened by the election of Maffeo Barberini, a friend and supporter of Galileo, as Pope Urban VIII in 1623. After a number of encouraging audiences with the new Pope, Galileo decided to go ahead with a major book on cosmology, entitled *Dialogue on the Two Great World Systems*. In it, Galileo has the relative merits of the Copernican and Ptolemaic theories discussed by three contrasting characters: Simplicio, a traditionalist; Sagredo, an open-minded man with intelligent questions; and Salviati, who usually speaks for Galileo himself.

In criticising the Ptolemaic theory, the book was probably attacking a position which had by that time been forsaken by most church astronomers, in favour of that of Tycho. It was the undisguised partiality of the *Dialogue* in favour of Copernicanism, however, which reaped a whirlwind. Galileo's enemies were incensed and the Pope, also of the opinion that Galileo had gone one step too far, unleashed the Inquisition.

In February 1633, at the age of 70, Galileo was summoned to Rome to stand before a tribunal of ten cardinals, accused of disobeying an injunction from the Pope that he should not teach the Copernican doctrine.

The outcome was a decree in June 1633, that 'Galileo Galilei…is to be interrogated concerning the accusation, even threatened with torture, and if he sustains it, proceeding to an abjuration of the vehement [suspicion of heresy] before the full Congregation of the Holy Office, sentenced to imprisonment.' [12]

The *Dialogue* was promptly banned.

Under the threat of torture, Galileo was forced into a humiliating abjuration of his previous opinions. 'I do not hold and have not held this opinion of Copernicus', he testified, 'since the command was intimated to me that I must abandon it.' [13]

Galileo was condemned to perpetual house arrest and forbidden to publish anything further upon the subject of cosmology. He was sent back to his house at Arceti, outside Florence, and there he remained until his death in 1642.

CHAPTER 6

ORBITS AND TRANSITS

When Copernicus and Galileo described the orbits of the inferior planets—Venus and Mercury—they were convinced that in a single orbit the planets would pass between the Earth and the Sun *only from east to west*. They would travel in the opposite direction—from west to east—only when they were *behind* the Sun. In theory, these planets might occasionally pass in front of the Sun's disc, but both Copernicus and Galileo were sceptical as to whether such an event would be noticeable.

In *De Revolutionibus*, Copernicus claimed that Venus and Mercury 'do not eclipse the Sun, because it rarely happens that they interfere with our view of the Sun, since they generally deviate in latitude. Besides, they are tiny bodies in comparison with the Sun. Venus, although bigger than Mercury can occult barely a hundredth of the Sun. So says Al-Battani of Racqua, who thinks that the Sun's diameter is ten times larger [than Venus'], and therefore so minute a speck is not easily descried in the most brilliant light. Yet in his *Paraphrase* of Ptolemy, Averroes reports having seen something blackish when he found a conjunction of the Sun and Mercury indicated in the tables.' [1]

The passage of a planet across the face of the Sun is called a 'transit' of the planet. Copernicus had successfully used the greatest elongation of Venus and Mercury to deduce the relative distances of those planets and the Earth from the Sun. He could not have guessed how the movement of Mercury, and more especially Venus, in transit, had the potential to yield a much richer harvest of information. In fact, such transits were to be the very means of determining the absolute distance of the Sun.

In order to understand how this could be so, we need to look in more detail at the orbits of the inferior planets.

The orbits of Mercury and Venus do not lie in the same plane as the Earth's orbit around the Sun.

Copernicus was mindful of this when he said that the planets and the Sun generally deviate in latitude when the planets are placed between the Earth and the Sun—that is, when an inferior conjunction is taking place. The planets, at such a time, do not necessarily lie on a *straight line* from the Earth to the Sun. Only when the inferior conjunction happens to take place virtually at the point where the planet's orbit crosses the Earth's orbital plane will the planet be on such a straight line. During this kind of conjunction there will be a transit—the planet *will* appear to cross the Sun's disc.

Inferior Planet	Inclination of Orbit (in degrees)
Mercury	7.0
Venus	3.4

Transits of Venus are very rare—much rarer than transits of Mercury. In fact, as we have seen, there hasn't been a transit of Venus since 1882. From the following diagram, it is clear that such a transit can only take place when Venus is near one of its *nodes*. The *nodes* are the points where the orbit of Venus (or any other planet) crosses the plane of the Earth's orbit. The *ascending node* is where the planet crosses from south to north; the *descending node* is where it crosses from north to south.

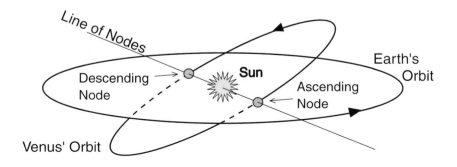

If we want to work out how frequently Venus will pass through the ascending node of its orbit, we shall need to know *how long* the planet takes to travel exactly once around the Sun: the *period* of revolution of Venus. A moment's thought will bring to light an immediate difficulty. We ourselves are not on a stationary observing platform, noting the date and time whenever Venus passes by. Rather, we are on the outside track, racing around the Sun, whilst every so often, Venus overtakes us on the inside track. The best we can do initially is to measure the interval between successive instances of overtaking. This time interval is known as the *synodic period* of the planet.

The synodic period is the time taken between successive appearances of a planet at the same point *relative to the Sun as seen from the Earth*. In the case of Venus, the period between successive inferior conjunctions—that is, the synodic period—is 583.92 days.

Since the synodic period of Venus is more than one Earth year and less than two Earth years, we can conclude that the Earth has been 'lapped' once. Venus repeats a passage through the ascending node of its orbit, however, only when it reaches the same point relative to a wider frame of reference— i.e. relative to the fixed stars. This period is known as the *sidereal period* of Venus.

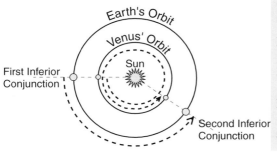

Synodic and Sidereal Periods

E = sidereal period of Earth

S = synodic period of Venus

P = sidereal period of Venus

and $1/P = 1/E + 1/S$

If all this is sounds a little daunting, fortunately there is a simple relationship between the synodic period and the sidereal period. This is shown in the above figure.

Given that the synodic period of Venus is 583.92 days and the sidereal period of the Earth is 365.256 days, then it can be shown that the sidereal period of Venus must be 224.701 days. Thus, Venus completes one orbit around the Sun in much less time than does the Earth. Every 224.701 days Venus passes through the ascending node of its orbit. At the opposite side of the orbit, also every 224.701 days, it passes down through the descending node.

If, at any of these times, the Earth is roughly in line with Venus and the Sun, there is a possibility of a transit taking place. A similar situation exists for the other inferior planet, Mercury, whose sidereal period is 89.969 days.

Copernicus doubted that either Venus or Mercury were large enough to *visibly* obscure part of the Sun's disc during transits. Galileo, writing to Mark Welser in 1612, was certain that they would be too small: 'The visible diameter of Venus is not even the sixth part of one minute, and its surface is less than one forty-thousandth that of the Sun...' Consequently, the passage of Venus would be impossible to discern against the Sun: '...one would seek in vain for such a tiny speck in its immense and gleaming face.' [2]

In the *Dialogue on the Two Chief World Systems*, which appeared in 1632, Galileo, through the character Salviati, tells his readers that Mercury is even smaller than Venus: 'its disc is so small and its brilliance so lively that the power of the telescope is not sufficient to strip off its hair so that it may appear completely shorn.' [3]

By the time the Dialogue emerged from the printing press, a transit of Mercury had been witnessed. Contrary to the expectations of Galileo, the clear outline of the planet, shorn of its 'hair', had been seen against the Sun. Astronomers had been alerted to the date, when such a transit would occur, by Kepler. For many years Kepler had held out the hope of observing transits. In early 1607, whilst he was still in the service of Rudolph II, drafting *New Astronomy*, his wish seemed about to be fulfilled.

CHAPTER 7

'A MOST AGREEABLE SPECTACLE'

A violent storm arose across Prague during the evening of 27th May 1607. With each flash of lightning, the Imperial Mathematician, Johannes Kepler, must have felt mounting excitement. Could the storm be a portent of the important astronomical event that he was expecting? Throughout April and May he had been keeping a watch on the planet Mercury in the evening sky. According to his calculations, it would be at inferior conjunction with the Sun on 29th May. Not suffering from the scepticism of Copernicus and Galileo, he suspected that it might actually be visible against the Sun's disc. The storm seemed like a premature confirmation of this. From time immemorial, astronomers had thought that important planetary conjunctions affected the weather, and Kepler was no exception. It is easy now to dismiss such ideas as primitive superstition or astrology, but, at the time, little was understood of meteorology and the causes of the weather. Little was known too of the physical influences emanating from heavenly bodies.

As soon as dawn broke the next day, Kepler and his friend Martin Bachazek made ready to observe the Sun for any unusual signs. The tail end of the storm had left the sky obscured by clouds. At length, their patience was rewarded: a gap in the clouds occurred and they eagerly clambered up to the darkened loft of the house that they shared. There, they held a piece of paper in the path of the Sun's rays, streaming through a narrow crack in the wall: in effect, a pin-hole camera. A small, crisp image of the Sun formed on the paper. The pair gasped in excitement as they observed on the image 'a little daub, quite black, approximately like a parched flea'. Kepler was convinced that he was watching a transit of Mercury. 'To make sure it was not a mark on the paper,' he later reported, "we kept moving the paper back and forth so that the light on the paper moved, and everywhere the little black spot appeared together with the light.' Elatedly, Kepler ran to let Emperor Rudolf II know what was happening. It always helps, to let your sponsor see a bit of the action! With one of the court mechanics, Kepler repeated the experiment: this time he covered the window in a workshop and let the sunlight shine through a tiny hole in a tin plate. The same phenomenon was to be seen: 'the little daub remained stationary in the light while the clouds moved over it'.[1]

Sadly, Kepler's elation was short-lived. He and his companion had not seen Mercury in transit at all. For them to have witnessed such a transit, the Earth would have to have been placed almost on the 'line of nodes' of Mercury's orbit. This line intersects the Earth's orbital path at two specific locations, therefore corresponding to two distinct times of the year. The required placement only occurs around the 7th November and 5th May (28th October and 25th April in the Julian calendar prevailing at the time): not even *near* the time of Kepler's and Bachazek's 'sighting'. What they had in fact seen was a large sunspot.

The existence of such blemishes on the Sun's disk was not 'discovered' until several years later, when Johannes Fabricius and Galileo observed them, using telescopes. 'Lucky I,' declared Kepler, undaunted, ten years later, 'who was the first in this century to have observed the spots'. [2]

The false sighting did not deter Kepler from further predictions at a later date, by which time he was armed with a more precise planetary theory. In 1629 he published an article—an *'Admonitio'*, or admonition—announcing that there would be a transit of Mercury on 7th November 1631 and urging others to watch for it. He did not live to see his prediction realised, but the event *did* happen and it *was* witnessed. In Paris, the astronomer Pierre Gassendi (1592–1655) earned renown by catching a glimpse of the spectacle.

Gassendi had been earnestly observing since the crack of dawn on the predicted day, but the weather was not obliging. Only at 9am did the clouds disperse sufficiently for him to behold the planet. He almost mistook the black dot, so small was it, for a sunspot. Kepler's mistake in reverse. He carefully measured the position of the spot so that it could be used as a reference marker. Not until a later break in the clouds did he realise its true nature. 'I could hardly persuade myself that it was Mercury,' he wrote, 'as my expectation of a larger magnitude bothered me, and I wondered if I had

Pierre Gassendi *(Courtesy of the Observatoire de Paris)*

been deceived in the previous measurement. But only when the sun shone again, I discovered further movement, and only then did I conclude that Mercury had come in on his splendid wings'. [3]

Fortunately, Gassendi had used a telescope to project the image of the Sun. If he had used Kepler's pin-hole method, he would probably not have seen Mercury, so small was its disc.

As Gassendi was making his observations of Mercury, an assistant, in the room beneath, faithfully measured the altitude of the Sun with a quadrant. Each time that Gassendi stamped on the ceiling a further reading was taken. Many found Gassendi's size for Mercury—less than one third of an arc-minute, scarcely one nineteenth of the Sun's diameter, compared with one fifteenth predicted by Kepler—hard to swallow. They claimed that he must have seen a sunspot rather than the planet, or that a trick of the light had made Mercury appear much smaller than its actual size.

Ultimately, none of the objections were sustainable. Gassendi's sighting represented a spectacular success for Kepler's *Rudolphine Tables*. It transpired that the tables of Ptolemy, Copernicus and Longomontanus had each been in error by about 5° in their prediction of Mercury's position at the time of

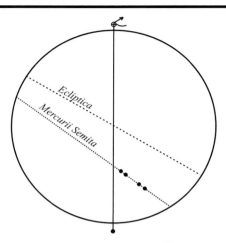

**The track of Mercury across the Sun observed by
Gassendi during the 1631 transit** *(based on a drawing in
his report 'Mercurius in Sole Visus et Venus Invisa')*

this transit, whereas Kepler's tables were accurate to within 10 minutes of arc: less than one third of the Sun's diameter!

In the same *Admonitio,* Kepler also predicted that a transit of Venus would take place in December 1631 and that Venus would appear to have a diameter one quarter that of the Sun. No-one observed it—due to the fact that it occurred after sunset for most of Europe. This was a cause for great regret, since he had also explained that transits of Venus involved a period of about 130 years and therefore the next one would not be until the mid-eighteenth century.

Only five months later, however, a young boy of thirteen or fourteen was admitted to Cambridge University, England, who would gain enduring fame by noticing a singular opportunity to observe a transit of Venus, not spotted by Kepler.

Very little is known about the short life of this gifted boy, Jeremiah Horrocks (c.1619–1641). He was born around 1619 in the Toxteth Park area of Liverpool. It is probable that his father was James Horrocks, a watchmaker, and that his mother was Mary Aspinwall. The family must have had only modest means, for Jeremiah entered Emmanuel College, Cambridge, as a *sizar* on 18th May 1632. A sizar was a student whose fees, or 'size', would be paid for by the University in return for work done in the College Kitchen, serving at tables or acting as a servant to Senior Fellows. A tiring way for a youngster to be expected to study.

Jeremiah's entry to the University at such a tender age was not unusual for the times. If he was conspicuous, it was for his preoccupations rather than his age. He was sufficiently interested in astronomy to be known to his fellow-students, perhaps disparagingly, as 'the curious astronomer'. In the acquisition of further knowledge in this field he was largely dependent upon his own endeavours. As yet, at Cambridge, there was neither a Professor of Mathematics, nor any teaching of the Sciences.

'There were many obstacles in the way', he wrote; 'the wearisome strain of the study with my mind untrained as yet, and my lack of means deterred and dispirited me ... But what grieved me most was that there was no one to instruct me in these arts nor anyone who could help me with sympathy in my endeavours; I was assailed by such torpor and dullness of mind. But what was I to do? It was not possible to ease the labour of my study, still less to increase my means; least of all could I implant in others the same love of Astronomy. But to give up the study of philosophy on account of the difficulties in my way was weak and unworthy of my soul. I decided, therefore, that weariness in study was to be overcome by industry; poverty by patience, since there was no other way; in default of a Master I must use astronomical books.' [4]

Fortunately, as we have already seen, Latin was the international language of scholarship and Horrocks, being already well-versed in the language, was able to read avidly the works of leading astronomical writers from around the world. His list of books still survives, hand-written by him in a copy of the Belgian Philip Van Lansberg's (1561–1632) astronomical tables, *Tabulae Motuum* (1632). Apart from the thirteenth century writer, John Holywood, better known by his latinised name Sacrobosco, not one of the books listed was by an English author.

When Horrocks left Cambridge in 1635, not having taken a degree, possibly forced to leave due to lack of financial support, he moved back to the Toxteth area.

He had become skilled in the use of Lansberg's tables and was fortunate enough to acquire a telescope for 'half a crown', with which he commenced making his own observations. The telescope was probably a 1½-inch diameter refractor, of the kind popularised by Galileo quarter of a century earlier. At first, the observations did not seem very successful. He discovered serious discrepancies between his observations and Lansberg's tables. Modestly, he put these down to his own lack of expertise. Around this time he made the acquaintance of William Crabtree (1610–1644), a draper from Broughton, near Manchester. The two became firm friends. Crabtree too was a keen observer of the night sky. On enquiry, Horrocks found that Crabtree's observations matched his own and concluded that the error was in Lansberg's tables, despite the author's boasts of accuracy. '...The very erroneous calculation of these tables...convinced me', Horrocks wrote, 'that an astronomer might be engaged upon a better work.' [5] He resolved to rely more upon his own skills as an observer and to re-examine the tables in a more critical light. He also made a concerted effort to compare the predictions of other published tables with his own data. Thus the Rudolphine Tables of Kepler, as well as the tables of Longomontanus and Copernicus, came under his scrutiny. He quickly became an enthusiastic advocate of Kepler's Laws of Planetary Motion—one of the first in England.

It was whilst scrutinising Lansberg's tables in this fashion, at the beginning of October 1639, that he became aware that there could soon be another conjunction of Venus with the Sun, as the planet passed through the ascending node of its orbit. Kepler's tables, which were generally far superior to Lansberg's, predicted that Venus would just miss crossing in front of the Sun's disc. Nevertheless, Horrocks quickly made his own calculations and concluded that, on this occasion at least, Lansberg had got it right. A transit across the Sun *was* likely to be seen. The prospect of being the first human being to witness such a remarkable event filled him with excitement.

All the useless computation with Lansberg's tables had not been in vain, after all. 'I pardon', he wrote, 'the miserable arrogance of the Belgian astronomer, who overloaded his useless Tables with such unmerited praise, and cease to lament the misapplication of my own time, deeming it a sufficient reward that I was thereby led to consider and forsee the appearance of Venus in the Sun.' [6]

He prepared assiduously for the predicted day, Sunday 24th November 1639 (old-style calendar), and also exhorted his younger brother, in Liverpool, and his friend Crabtree, in Manchester, to make similar preparations. Other friends, he guessed, would 'care little for trifles of this kind, preferring rather their hawks and their hounds, to say no worse.' [7]

His letter of 26th October to Crabtree explained: 'The reason why I am writing to you now is to warn you of the remarkable conjunction of the Sun and Venus which will take place on November 24, on which date Venus will transit the solar disc. This has not occurred for many years and will not occur again in this century. I therefore beg you most urgently to watch carefully with your telescope and to make whatever observation you can, especially as to the diameter of Venus which Kepler put at 7', Lansberg at 11', while I make it scarcely more than 1'.' [8]

Horrocks' own observation was to be from 'an obscure village where I have long been in the habit of observing, about fifteen miles north of Liverpool'. [9] There is a strong tradition that this meant the village now known as Much Hoole and that his observations were carried out from a first floor window of Carr House, near there.

In a later account, entitled *Venus in Sole Visa* (Venus Seen upon the Sun), sprinkled with flowery verses, Horrocks described his method of observing the transit: 'I described on a sheet of paper a circle whose diameter was

Carr House from where Horrocks is thought to have made his observations

nearly equal to six inches, the narrowness of the apartment not permitting me conveniently to use a larger size…I divided the circumference of this circle into 360° in the usual manner, and its diameter into thirty equal parts…each of these thirty parts was again divided into four equal portions, making in all one hundred and twenty…the rest I left to ocular computation…when the time of the observation approached, I retired to my apartment, and having closed the windows against the light, I directed my telescope, previously adjusted to a focus, through the aperture towards the sun and received his rays at right angles upon the paper already mentioned. The sun's image exactly filled the circle, and I watched carefully and unceasingly for any dark body that might enter upon the disc of light.' [10]

Although not expecting the transit to take place until the 24th of the month, he was aware that some tables predicted the conjunction of Venus with the Sun to take place the previous day. Leaving nothing to chance, he made an early start: 'I was unwilling to depend entirely on my own opinion which was not sufficiently confirmed, lest by too much self confidence I might endanger the observation. Anxiously intent therefore on the undertaking through the greater part of the 23rd, and the whole of the 24th, I omitted no available opportunity of observing her ingress. I watched carefully on the 24th from sunrise to nine o'clock, and from a little before ten until noon, and at one in the afternoon, being called away in the intervals by business of the highest importance which, for these ornamental pursuits, I could not with propriety neglect.' [11]

Opinions differ as to what business could have been so important that Horrocks would have been prepared to jeopardise his observation of such a rare event on account of it. Some say that he was a curate with a service to conduct at Hoole church, given that the day was the Christian Sabbath: Others, pointing to strong evidence of an existing incumbent of that post, speculate that he was, being an educated young man, perhaps a lay reader at the same church. The piety embodied in his writings leaves no doubt that the business at hand would have been of a religious character.

Whatever the reason for the interruption, after a fruitless morning's watch, Horrocks must have been desperate to get back to the darkened apartment: 'About fifteen minutes past three in the afternoon, when I was again at liberty to continue my labours, the clouds, as if by divine interposition, were entirely

The Founder of English Astronomy, by Eyre Crowe (1874–1910). A Nineteenth Century painting of Horrocks observing the transit *(Courtesy of Board of Trustees of the National Museums and Galleries on Merseyside (Walker Art Gallery))*

dispersed, and I was once more invited to the grateful task of repeating my observations. I then beheld a most agreeable spectacle, the object of my sanguine wishes, a spot of unusual magnitude and of a perfectly circular shape, which had already fully entered upon the sun's disc on the left, so that the limbs of the Sun and Venus precisely coincided, forming an angle of contact. Not doubting that this was really the shadow of the planet, I immediately applied myself sedulously to observe it.' [12]

Between that first sighting and sunset, thirty-five minutes later, Horrocks recorded, in all, three distinct observations of Venus, noting for each one the time and the precise position of Venus on the Sun's disc. He also estimated the diameter of Venus, which was 'larger indeed than the thirtieth part of the solar diameter, though not more so than the sixth or at the utmost the fifth, of such a part.' [13] Given that the Sun's diameter on that day was estimated to be 31'30", he took the diameter of Venus to be 1'16".

Half-an-hour was not long to gather the measurements which he desired. Nevertheless, Horrocks, with an understandable sense of relief, considered that 'all the observations which could possibly be made in so short a time, I was enabled, by Divine Providence, to complete so effectually that I could scarcely have wished for a more extended period.' [14]

What about his co-observers? His brother's efforts in Liverpool were completely thwarted by cloudy skies. He failed to catch even a glimpse. Meanwhile, in Manchester, Crabtree almost suffered the same fate. After watching earnestly for most of the day, he had all but given up in despair when, less than fifteen minutes before sunset, according to Horrocks, 'the Sun bursting forth from behind the clouds, he at once began to observe, and was gratified by beholding the pleasing spectacle of Venus upon the Sun's disc. Rapt in contemplation, he stood for some time motionless, scarcely trusting his own senses, through an excess of joy.' [15]

Within moments the awesome sight was gone, as the Sun was once again wrapped in clouds. Crabtree, although a serious astronomer, had found the experience so moving that he had failed to take any measurements of the position of Venus. Still, he did confirm that the planet's shadow was indeed

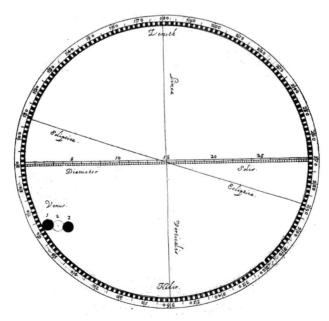

Horrocks' observations of Venus in transit across the face of the Sun, as reproduced by Hevelius *(Mercurius in Sole visus Gedani)*

as tiny as Horrocks had both forecast and noted: Crabtree made its diameter to be in the ratio 7 to 200 to that of the Sun. In other words, subtending an angle of about 1'3" to the eye of the beholder.

If Horrocks felt disappointed by his friend's performance, he gave no hint of it. He completely understood how Crabtree was so overcome: 'We astronomers,' he wrote, '…are overjoyed with trifles and such small matters as scarcely make an impression upon others; a susceptibility which those who will may deride with impunity, even in my own presence, and, if it gratify them, I too will join in the merriment.' [16]

William Crabtree's observation (mural painting by Ford Madox Brown, displayed in Manchester Town Hall)

As to his own observations, he had good reason to feel satisfied. Careful preparations for the transit had enabled him to secure measurements that would greatly improve knowledge about the orbit of Venus. The path of Venus across the Sun's disk provided sufficient information for him to calculate the precise point at which the planet would cross the Sun's path: that is, the location of the *ascending node* of Venus' orbit. He also determined the corrections needed to bring Kepler's tables into line with the observations. Chief amongst these was a change to the mean radius of Venus' orbit, compared with that of the Earth. In the Rudolphine Tables, Kepler had fixed the respective distances in the ratio of 72,414 to 100,000: Horrocks reduced it to 72,333 to 100,000.

The corrected radius of Venus' orbit given by Horrocks—0.72333 AU (astronomical units)—is exactly the value given in modern tables of planetary orbits. The *astronomical unit* is, by definition, the mean distance of the Earth from the Sun. Therefore, any distances measured in this unit are simply *relative* distances. Venus was thereby stated to be orbiting the Sun at a mean distance 72.333% of that of our own planet, the Earth.

What was the absolute distance of the planets from the Sun? No one knew. The entire theoretical edifice of Copernicus and Kepler was based on the *relative* distances of each planet from the Sun, not *absolute* distances.

Of course, the distance to the Sun—one AU—was known to be immense. Around the year 1640, the Belgian astronomer Gottfried Wendelin (1580–1667) used a telescope to repeat the famous dichotomy method used by Aristarchus in ancient times to obtain the ratio of the distances to the Moon and Sun. He found that the angle between the centres of the quarter Moon and the Sun was 89¾° . Consequently, the Sun was shown to be 229 times further away than the Moon. This was twelve times greater than the figure derived by Aristarchus, but still gave no clue about how many miles or kilometres it was to the Sun.

Many educated guesses were made about the absolute distance. It was customary for these to be expressed in terms of the *solar parallax*. As explained previously, this quantity is actually an angle: the angle which would be formed between two lines, the one projected from an observer at the centre of the Sun to the centre of the Earth, and the other projected from the same observer to the outer edge of the Earth. Since the distance from the centre of the Earth to its outer edge, the radius, was already well-established, knowing the solar parallax, would allow the distance between the Earth and the Sun to be easily calculated.

Estimates of the solar parallax made by Aristarchus, Hipparchus and Ptolemy, more than fifteen hundred years earlier, were still current in the seventeenth century. Even the great observational astronomer Tycho Brahe accepted Ptolemy's value of 3', which implied that the Sun was about 1145 semi-diameters of the Earth away. In the years which followed, however, estimates of this angle decreased its magnitude dramatically. Johannes Kepler derived a solar parallax of less than 1' from his observations of Mars, implying a distance of about 3450 Earth semi-diameters. Thus the Sun itself was judged to be further and further from the Earth. As a corollary, the Sun was becoming even more immense relative to the Earth.

The concluding chapter of Horrocks treatise, *Venus in Sole Visa*, was grandly entitled *Of the Diameters of the rest of the Planets, of the Proportions of the Celestial Spheres, and of the Parallax of the Sun*. In it he used his observations of Venus to deduce a startling new value for the solar parallax. 'I shall here say something which may tend', he commenced cautiously, 'to throw light upon the dimensions of the stars, and upon the horizontal parallax of the Sun, a matter of the greatest importance, and one which has been the subject of much fruitless speculation; but I will not speak dogmatically, nor, as I may say, "ex cathedra", but rather for the sake of promoting discussion...'[17]

His reasoning went as follows:

From the corrected version of Kepler's tables, the Earth-Venus distance at the time of the transit was 0.26409 AU and, at this distance, Venus appeared to have an angular size of 1'16". Therefore, seen from the Sun, when at its mean distance, 0.72333 AU, Venus must appear to be smaller, in proportion to the greater distance—i.e. 1'16" multiplied by 0.26409/0.72333. Thus, the apparent size of Venus would be 28" and its radius, or semi-diameter, would be 14".

Horrocks felt sure that the real diameters of the planets must bear some relationship to the diameters of their orbits. He had noticed also that, allowing for observational errors, the other planets could be shown, from measurements by Remus, Kepler, Tycho and Gassendi, to have a similar angular size to Venus, if considered from the vantage point of the Sun.

Having started modestly and without dogma, Horrocks changed tack: 'Since therefore it is certain that the diameters of the five primary planets, in mean distance, appear from the Sun 0'28", and that none of them deviate from this rule, tell me, ye followers of Copernicus, for I esteem not the opinions of others, tell me what prevents our fixing the diameter of the Earth at the same measurement, the parallax of the Sun being nearly 0'14" at a distance, in round numbers, of 15,000 of the Earth's semi-diameters.'[18] With these words, the previous best published estimates of the Sun's distance were increased four-fold, to almost 95 million kilometres (60 million miles).

His assumption that all the planets subtend the same angle at the Sun was unfounded and untrue. Nevertheless, it did come fairly close to the truth for

Mercury, Venus and the Earth. Consequently, his values for the solar parallax and the astronomical unit were much more accurate than any calculated hitherto. It is remarkable to consider that this result was obtained by a twenty-one year old youth. A youth moreover who was largely self-taught.

In addition to his observation of the transit of Venus, Horrocks made other discoveries of lasting significance, relating to the motion of the Moon and the planets. Included in these were the demonstration, at the age of 18, that the Moon moved in an elliptical orbit about the Earth. 'Our countryman, Horrocks,' acknowledged Isaac Newton, 'was the first who advanced the theory of the Moon's moving in an ellipse about the Earth placed in its lower focus.' [19]

These achievements at such a tender age held out immense promise for his future contribution to Science. This promise, alas, was not to be fulfilled. Intending to discuss with Crabtree possible publishers for his treatise on the transit of Venus, Horrocks wrote to his friend on 19th December 1640, fixing the 4th January 1641 as the date for a meeting, 'if nothing unforseen should occur.' On the day before the intended meeting, tragically, aged only twenty-two, Horrocks suddenly died. There is no surviving record of the cause of death.

Crabtree was devastated. Many years later, a bundle of Horrocks' letters was found amongst Crabtree's papers. On the back of the last letter, in Crabtree's handwriting, was discovered the touching inscription: 'Letters of Mr. Jeremiah Horrox to me, of the years 1638, 1639, 1640, until his death on the morning of the 3rd January, when he expired very suddenly, the day before he had proposed coming to me. Thus God puts an end to all worldly affairs! and I am, alas! bereaved of my dearest Horrox. Irreparable loss! Hence these tears!' [20]

The arrangements for publication of his treatise on the transit of Venus were still incomplete. Horrocks' life was all too brief and his achievements were known only to a handful of people. Few appreciated the importance of his papers and, upon his death, many were destroyed. His friend William Crabtree managed to rescue a number of papers, but he too was to die tragically within three years, a victim of the English Civil War. Additional papers were rescued by Jeremy Shakerley, but these perished subsequently in the Great Fire of London of 1666. Some were taken to Ireland by his brother, Jonas, but when he died they disappeared. Yet other papers of Horrocks were plundered, from his father's house in Toxteth, by soldiers during the Civil War and committed to the flames.

After Crabtree's death the papers, which he had saved, including the treatise on Venus, were bought by John Worthington, who had been a contemporary of Horrocks at Emmanuel College. In 1660 a copy of *Venus in Sole Visa* came into the possession of the Dutch astronomer Christian Huygens (1629–1695), who passed it to Johannes Hevelius (1611–1687) in Danzig (Gdansk). Two years later, Hevelius published the treatise, together with his own account of the 1661 transit of Mercury, *Mercurius in Sole visus Gedani*. Thus, against the odds, Horrocks' trail-blazing account was rescued from oblivion. In 1664 the Royal Society, in London, agreed to publish Horrocks' surviving papers, but due to lack of funds, they were not published until 1672, over thirty years after their author's demise.

The body of Jeremiah Horrocks is thought to lie in an unmarked grave in the grounds of the Parish Church of St.Michael in Liverpool. Such was the affection in which his memory was held by generations of astronomers, that near the time of a later transit of Venus, in 1874, a monument to him was erected in Westminster Abbey. The inscription on the monument eloquently recalls his achievements:

In Memory of Jeremiah Horrocks
Curate of Hoole in Lancashire
Who died on the 3rd of January 1641 in or near his 22nd year
Having in so short a life
Detected the long inequality in the mean motion of Jupiter and Saturn
Discovered the orbit of the Moon to be an ellipse
Determined the motion of the lunar apse
Suggested the physical cause of its revolution
and predicted from his own observations the Transit of Venus
which was seen by himself and his friend William Crabtree
On Sunday the 24th of November (O.S.) 1639

Over the monument in keeping with the ecclesiastical setting, and in the original Latin, is Horrocks' pious disclosure about being called away from his observations by 'business of the highest importance', which he could not neglect: *Aliis temporibus ad majora avocatus quae ob haec parerga negligi non decuit.*

CHAPTER 8

PREDICTING TRANSITS OF VENUS

Oh! then farewell thou beauteous Queen! thy sway
May soften nations yet untamed, whose breasts
Bereft of native fury then shall learn
The milder virtues. We with anxious mind
Follow thy latest footsteps here, and far
As thought can carry us; my labours now
Bedeck the monument for future times
Which thou at parting left us. Thy return
Posterity shall witness; years must roll
Away, but then at length the splendid sight
Again shall greet our distant children's eyes.

-Jeremiah Horrocks (Venus in Sole Visa) [1]

The key to Horrocks' success was his accurate prediction of the 1639 transit of Venus. Such transits occur with what may seem at first sight a strange periodicity. The dates (new style) of all the transits from the seventeenth century through to the twenty-first century are shown below.

Transits of Venus take place in pairs. In each pair the transits are separated by eight years and are associated with the same node. There then follows a gap of more than a century, after which a pair occur at the other node. Ascending node transits occur in December and descending node transits in June.

The accurate prediction of the exact dates and times of transits involves some pretty heavy mathematics: not the kind of thing for the faint-hearted. Nevertheless, a rough explanation of the basic pattern is accessible, if we make some simplifying assumptions: namely, that the orbits of the Earth and Venus are concentric circles and that the node positions of Venus do not shift. These are not strictly true, but are near enough to the truth to suit our purpose.

Date	Node	Interval (years)
1631 December 7	Ascending	
		8
1639 December 4	Ascending	
		121½
1761 June 6	Descending	
		8
1769 June 3	Descending	
		105½
1874 December 9	Ascending	
		8
1882 December 6	Ascending	
		121½
2004 June 8	Descending	
		8
2012 June 5 - 6	Descending	

Transits of Venus: 1631-2012

Let us consider a time at which the Earth, Venus and the Sun are in line at the ascending node of Venus. In other words, we envisage a moment during which, seen from the centre of the Earth, a perfectly central transit of Venus is taking place.

Such an exact conjunction of the planet with the Sun will occur again only when Venus has completed an *integral,* or whole, number of orbits *and* the Earth too has completed an *integral* number of orbits. Thus both will have returned to the same place. If these integral numbers are n and N respectively, then equating the number of days taken for so many orbits gives,

$$224.701\, n = 365.25636\, N.$$

This is because the sidereal year of Venus is 224.701 days and that of the Earth is 365.25636 days.

This expression, or formula, is not commensurable. In other words, for whole number, or integral, values of n and N—1,2,3,4,5, etc—the equation is never exactly satisfied. Equality almost occurs for the values of n and N given in the following table.

Number of Earth Orbits	Number of Venus Orbits	Difference (hours)	Interval (years)
0	0	0	
			8
8	13	22.5	
			227
235	382	12.9	
			8
243	395	9.6	
			235
478	777	3.3	

Ascending Node near-alignments

The gaps between these alignments, in Earth years (or Earth orbits), are too large to explain the actual dates of Venus transits. We must remember, however, that alignments can also take place at the *descending* node, at the opposite side of the Sun, when the orbit of Venus takes it downward through the plane of the Earth's orbit.

These alignments must occur at an integral number of orbits, of the Earth and Venus, plus a half orbit, after passing the starting point which we initially considered. The equivalent equation then is,

$$224.701 \, (n + \tfrac{1}{2}) = 365.25636 \, (N + \tfrac{1}{2}).$$

For 121½ Earth orbits and 197½ Venus orbits (i.e. $N=121$ and $n=197$) the equation is almost satisfied. Only 4.8 hours separates the two sides of the equation.

The descending node transits occur at the same 8, 235 and 243 year intervals as the ascending node ones, but a gap of 121½ years separates an ascending node pair from the following descending node pair. The overall result is shown in the following diagram.

93

	Ascending to Ascending	Ascending to Descending	Descending to Descending	Overall Pattern
1631 Dec [A]	8			8
1639 Dec [A]				
		121.5		121.5
1761 Jun [D]	243		8	8
1769 Jun [D]				
	235			
			243	105.5
1874 Dec [A]				
	8		235	8
1882 Dec [A]				
		121.5		121.5
2004 Jun [D]				
			8	8
2012 Jun [D]				

The transits of Venus from 1631 to 2012

As Venus travels along its orbit around the Sun, it casts a gigantic conical shadow out into the Solar System. This shadow is chasing after the Earth, gaining at a rate of more than 40,000 miles per hour. Occasionally, near the nodes, as explained, the Earth gets caught in the shadow. That is when a transit is seen: if the Earth is in the shadow of Venus, then Venus must be, at least to some degree, interposed between the Sun's disk and the Earth. Venus need not be *exactly* at one of the nodes, because the shadow is enormous. By the time it has stretched out to reach the Earth's orbital path, the diameter of the shadow is more than 300,000 miles! In fact, Venus can be more than two days away from passing through the nodes of its orbit when a transit takes place. Much more than two days and the shadow will have moved too far above or below the plane of the Earth's orbit to have any chance of touching the Earth.

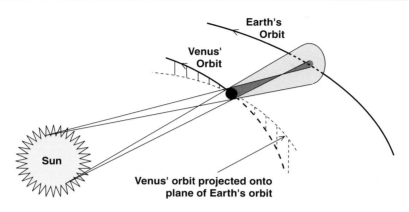

Perspective view of the shadow cone cast by Venus

The shadow cone really consists of two parts: an outer cone, or *penumbra*, and an inner cone, the *umbra*. As the edge of the outer cone (point 'a' on the plan view below) first passes over an earth-bound observer, s/he sees Venus entirely to the east of the Sun, but just touching the outside of the Sun's edge, or limb. In other words, Venus and the Sun appear at opposite sides of the line aE. This is the moment of first contact, or 'external contact at ingress'.

As the edge of the inner cone (point 'b') first passes over the observer, Venus and the Sun both appear on the same side of line bE. Venus is therefore just touching the inside of the Sun's limb and is completely on the Sun's disk. This is the moment of second contact, or 'internal contact at ingress'. The same situation occurs in reverse at points 'c' and 'd', as Venus leaves the

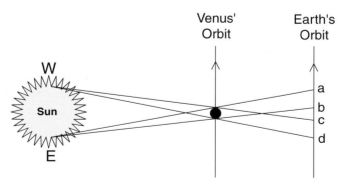

Plan view of the shadow cone cast by Venus (viewed from the north)

Sun. These points represent the moments of third and fourth contact—or internal and external contacts at egress.

The observer's view of Venus at each of these contacts would be similar to that shown below.

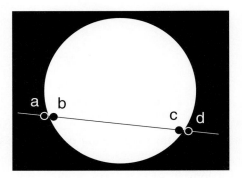

Jeremiah Horrocks, of course, saw only one of these moments of contact with the limb of the Sun. His meticulous record of what he did see, however, was vital in enabling future astronomers to predict where, on the Earth's surface, *they* would have to be in order to see the whole process.

CHAPTER 9

TO THE FOUR CORNERS OF THE EARTH

By the late seventeenth century, a striking paradox had arisen concerning the progress of astronomy compared with that of its sister science, navigation. It had become possible for astronomers, armed with the observations of Gassendi, Horrocks and others, to predict transits with a fair degree of accuracy. It was even possible to pin-point where, on the Earth's globe, one would need to be to see the full duration of such transits. It was unbelievably difficult, nevertheless, for those heading for such places, to know when they were anywhere near! Navigators could never be sure of their exact position. Many a time their ships would unexpectedly crash into the rocky outposts of their destinations in the middle of the night, or, maybe, overshoot by hundreds of miles.

So long as sailors did not venture far beyond the coast, there was no problem. The age-old technique known as *dead-reckoning* sufficed. A navigator could keep account of a ship's position by noting regularly its bearing and speed. For the bearing, the magnetic needle of a compass was used. For the speed, a log or lump of wood, attached to a rope, was thrown overboard and the length of rope which was run out in half a minute, timed with a sandglass, would give an indication of speed. To assist in measuring this length, knots would be tied in the rope every seven fathoms (1 fathom = 1.8 metres). It was from this technique that the term 'knots' for the speed of a ship was derived.

But dead-reckoning was too crude for long journeys. As soon as the great sea-faring nations began to take to the high seas—in search of new worlds, bold trade routes, or simply conquest—the story was different. It then became crucial to know a ship's exact position at any time: its longitude and latitude.

There was nothing new about longitude and latitude. The basic concepts had been handed down by the Ancient Greeks. Faced with the problem of describing the position of known places on the curved surface of the Earth, pioneers, like Eratosthenes, Hipparchus and Ptolemy, devised the familiar system of criss-cross lines, which is still used today. It can be seen on any school-room globe.

The lines of longitude—or meridian lines—are great circles, passing through the North and South Poles, dividing the Earth into thin segments, like those of an orange. The Earth rotates about an axis which passes through the poles. Consequently, if we follow a portion of any particular meridian line, on its journey from north to south, we find that every point along the line experiences noon—that is, it directly faces the Sun—at the same time. In one sense, no meridian line is any more important than another. But the whole point of the scheme is to describe where one location is relative to another: how far it is 'offset' from a reference location. In practice therefore, one meridian is defined as the 'prime' meridian—the 'first among equals'.

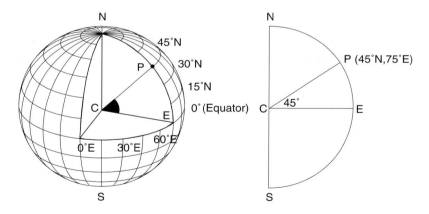

In Antiquity, a meridian passing through the Fortunate Islands (now known as the Canaries) was the prime meridian and all locations were measured eastward from this meridian. References to the Fortunate Islands continued almost up to the eve of modern times. Even in Horrock's treatise on the 1639 transit of Venus, care was taken to cite the difference in longitude (22½°) between the Fortunate Islands and his observing site in the village of Hoole. Since 1884, the meridian running through the Greenwich Observatory, in England, has been accepted internationally as the prime meridian (largely because 65% of ships were already using it as such). The longitude of any place is defined as the angle through which its meridian appears to be rotated, about the polar axis, to the west or east of the Greenwich meridian.

The position of a place on the Earth's surface is only partly given by its longitude. To fully tie down the position, we need to state *where* it is on its meridian line: how far north or south of the Equator. Stating its latitude does this. Consider a line stretched between the chosen place and the centre of the Earth. The latitude of the place is the angle at which this line is inclined, above or below, the plane of the Equator.

For the seventeenth century sailor, working out the latitude of a ship was child's play. For every degree of latitude that the ship sailed northward, any given star, as it crossed over the ship's meridian, would appear to be one degree nearer the southern horizon. There was no difficulty in using this fact to get the latitude. Longitude however was a big head-ache. A practical method for determining the longitude of a ship at sea, still seemed far out of reach.

'Pilots content themselves with knowledge of the latitude', wrote Pigafetta—a companion of the great Portuguese captain, Magellan—'and are so proud, they will not hear speak of the longitude.' [1] But the losses of ships, cargoes and lives was too great to allow this 'proud' ignorance to prevail. Throughout the seventeenth century, and beyond, tantalising prizes were on offer to anyone who could discover a method of determining the longitude at sea. In 1598, Philip III of Spain promised a perpetual pension of 6000 ducats and a life pension of 2000 ducats. The governments of Portugal, and Holland too offered handsome rewards.

Many of the finest minds of the period were exercised on the problem. But to no avail. The longitude stubbornly refused to succumb to their efforts. The quest to find the longitude became synonymous with futile endeavour.

One foggy night, in the year 1707, a whole squadron of Royal Navy ships, led by Admiral Sir Cloudisley Shovell, struck rocks off the Scilly Isles, resulting in the loss of almost 2,000 lives. In response to the public outcry following this tragedy, the British Parliament set up a panel of experts, the Board of Longitude, to look urgently at the whole problem. They also proposed substantial prizes: £20,000 to anyone who could demonstrate a method of determining longitude at sea, to within half a degree; £15,000 for a method to within two-thirds of a degree; and £10,000 for a method to within one degree.

All sorts of weird and wonderful ideas were summoned up by the lure of money. Some were simply impractical: such as, barges moored at set points around the world, all firing flare rockets into the sky at midnight. Others were plain barmy. Into the latter category must be placed the oft-cited 'Powder of Sympathy'. One person claimed to have discovered a powder which, when it was sprinkled on a knife which had inflicted a wound, would cause the pain brought about by the wound to recur. Therefore, it was suggested, a multitude of dogs, all wounded by the same knife, could be taken on board different ships. Powder of Sympathy could be brought into contact with the knife at noon in Greenwich and this would cause all the dogs, at their far flung locations, to yelp simultaneously. As we shall see, knowledge of the time *was* an important ingredient of any attempt to crack the longitude problem. Needless to say, the Powder of Sympathy had no part to play.

The problem of longitude could be reduced to the problem of accurately measuring time. If a navigator was able to determine the time at which a particular star crossed his meridian, and also knew the time when the same star passed over the meridian at some other point—say Greenwich—then the difference in longitude of the two places could be calculated from the difference in time. Every point on the Earth's surface is rotating around the polar axis at the rate of one degree of rotation every four minutes of time. Consequently, if a given star passes across a navigator's meridian 40 minutes later than a star 'catalogue' shows it passing over the Greenwich meridian, the navigator must be situated at a longitude 10 degrees west of Greenwich.

So, we might conclude, all that was needed for determining the longitude was a star catalogue, a good clock and, of course, a clear, starlit night. Maybe so, but the provision of the clock was no simple matter. The clock, if the star catalogue was from Greenwich, needed to show Greenwich time. It needed to be synchronised at Greenwich and then taken on board ship, to be available whenever the longitude was required. Herein lay the difficulty for navigators.

Transporting a clock out to sea, in the seventeenth century, was almost guaranteed to wreck its timekeeping capabilities. Christian Huygens, the inventor, in 1657, of the pendulum clock, made a valiant attempt at designing sea-going clocks, but without much success. In 1668, one of his clocks sailed through gales and even a sea battle and still managed to keep going. However, the difference of longitude between Toulon and Crete, established on this voyage, using the clock, was 20°30' instead of the correct value of 19°13'. The implied error in distance was more than 60 miles: ample discrepancy to produce disaster at sea. In 1691, several British men-of-war were wrecked off Plymouth due to a mistaken idea of their position; in 1694, Admiral Wheeler's squadron of ships ran aground at Gibraltar, thinking that they had already passed through the Strait after leaving the Mediterranean. Knowing the correct time, in order to know the longitude, was a life-and-death matter.

Not until a century after Huygen's invention, would clocks be available, made by Pierre Le Roy and John Harrison, which could keep sufficiently good time at sea. Meanwhile, work continued apace on the other pre-requisite: accurate star catalogues. National observatories were set up with the specific aim of assisting navigation, by compiling just such catalogues. The observatory at Greenwich was founded in 1675 by the Royal Warrant of King Charles II.

'In order to the finding out of the longitude of places for perfecting navigation and astronomy,' ran the King's Warrant, 'we have resolved to build a small observatory within Our Park at Greenwich upon the highest ground at or near the Place where the Castle stood, with lodging rooms for Our Astronomical Observator and Assistant.' [2] John Flamsteed (1646–1720) was appointed as the said 'Observator'—the first Astronomer Royal—to take charge of the venture.

In Paris, the Observatoire Royale had been established eight years earlier, in 1667, by Louis XIV, for similar purposes. Here Gian Domenico Cassini (1625–1712) was appointed as the first director.

Cassini was an astronomer of the first rank. One of his key contributions was to publish, in 1668, ephemerides for the moons of Jupiter: tables of times for the eclipsing of the moons by Jupiter's shadow. Sixteen years of hard graft and patient observation had gone into their production. The result was highly significant, for, equipped with these tables, an astronomer, or indeed, a navigator, could use Jupiter and its moons as a 'clock in the sky'— a clock moreover, which told the same time wherever you happened to be on the Earth's surface. The moons disappeared so instantaneously as they entered

Jupiter's shadow, and emerged so suddenly out of it, that astronomers could judge the time of the event to within half a second of time. These eclipses were particularly convenient, as they happened almost every day. The only drawback, and it was an important one, was that it was completely impractical to view the satellites from the rolling deck of a ship. Only on land did observation of this 'universal clock', coupled with Cassini's tables, allow the longitude to be calculated.

Centuries earlier, suggestions had been made that the movement of the Moon against the starry background could be used similarly as a 'universal clock'. The motion of the Moon, however, was exceedingly complex and insufficiently understood to make this method viable. Even the incomparable Isaac Newton (1643–1727) once admitted in despair that lunar theory made his head ache and kept him awake at nights.

Eclipses of the Moon could be used to compare times at different observing locations, but these were too infrequent to provide much assistance to navigators.

Meanwhile, adventurous sea-farers coped as best they could. The wide world beckoned and, undaunted, they navigated the high seas, reaching their distant destinations through a combination of intuition, skill and sheer good luck. They were joined in the 1670s by a new breed of passenger: the scientific expeditionary. Enthusiastic astronomers, often dispatched by the fledgling scientific institutions of their motherlands, ventured to the four corners of the Earth. They hoped to contribute something to the understanding of the heavens—and possibly, thereby, to help solve the problems of navigation.

First in a long line was the French astronomer, Jean Richer (1630–1696). His expedition to the island of Cayenne (1672–73) was primarily for the purpose of observing the stars and planets, but is mostly remembered for a purely accidental discovery. On arriving at the island—on the coast of present-day French Guiana, in South America—he set up a pendulum clock. The clock had been perfectly regulated before departure from Paris, but in Cayenne, not far from the Equator, it lost more than two minutes a day. Only by significantly shortening its pendulum was Richer able to restore accurate timekeeping. The amount of shortening was far more than would have been necessary simply to compensate for the increased centrifugal force at the Equator. The slow-down of Richer's pendulum provided powerful evidence that the Earth's radius was greater at the Equator than in higher latitudes. In other words, the Earth was not a perfect sphere. In effect, it was an oblate shape.

Barely three years after Richer's return to France, a memorandum received by Sir Joseph Williamson, the English Secretary of State, announced another expedition to southern latitudes for the purpose of astronomical observation: 'Edmund Halley, student at Queen's College, Oxford, having been for some years a diligent observer of the planets and stars, has found it absolutely necessary, besides the continuance of observations here, that in some place betwixt the Tropics, where the sun, moon and planets will pass near the zenith without refraction, their motions will be much better ascertained and navigation perfected, and that St.Helena will be a fit place, where the celestial globe may be finished, the stars in the southern hemisphere being very much out of their places. He humbly desires His Majesty's letter of recommendation to the East India Company, that they will cause the ship ready to go to St.Helena to transport him and his friend thither, and that they may be received and entertained and have some fitting assistance.' [3]

It was perhaps a sign of the extreme importance attached by the State, at that time, to the problems of navigation—as well as to the supplicant's highly placed connections—that this audacious request to the King, from a mere undergraduate, met with complete success. None of those giving their blessing, however, could have foreseen how the intended expedition would prove to be seminal in the human quest to find the distance of the Sun.

CHAPTER 10

HALLEY'S ADMONITION

It is difficult to imagine a more isolated place than the tiny island of St. Helena: the eroded summit of an extinct volcano, rearing out of the ocean, 1200 miles off the west coast of Africa. This was the destination of the East India Company's ship, *Unity*, as it quietly slid out of the River Thames one winter's day in 1676. On board the ship were the twenty year old Edmond Halley (1656–1742) and his friend, Clerk. Their unusual baggage included: an iron-framed sextant—5½ feet in radius; a 24-foot long telescope; a pendulum clock and several other astronomical instruments.

As they watched the ship's sails filling in the wind and heard the creak of its timbers in response to the Atlantic heave, the young men must have wondered, with some trepidation, what was in store for them. Long distance voyages at that time always carried a large element of risk. The twin threats of shipwreck and disease were never far away. Even the possibility of attack by pirates could not be ignored. Only a few months earlier, Halley's close friend, Charles Boucher, bound for Jamaica, had been shipwrecked in the West Indies. Fortunately, he had been rescued, but then the rescue ship had been captured by privateers.

Whatever fear Halley may have harboured, was quickly evaporated by his burning enthusiasm for scientific discovery. 'I promise myself that I shall be able to do something acceptable to the learned world' [1], he had recently confided to the Royal Society's Secretary.

This was no futile ambition. Halley's name would later be immortalised by association with the spectacular comet, but already he had come to the notice of the scientific community in England, as a young man of exceptional promise. The Astronomer Royal, John Flamsteed, said in the summer of the previous year: 'I have…met with a ingenious youth versed in calculations and almost all parts of mathematics, though yet scarce 19 years of age; Mr. Edmond Halley, whose assistance I hope to have often since he lives most commonly in the city and we agree exceedingly well in our thoughts concerning the most convenient and useful method.' [2]

Even at the age of nineteen, Halley had submitted a much admired paper to the Royal Society, explaining how to determine the true orbit of a celestial body from observation. Now he was determined to play a more prominent role.

As a result of the work at observatories such as those at Greenwich and Paris, northern hemisphere star catalogues were well underway. From St. Helena, Halley was intent on mapping the southern skies. The island was 16 degrees south of the Equator and from this vantage point he would be able to observe stars, including the south polar stars, which were forever invisible to Europe. He had considered going to the Cape of Good Hope or Rio de Janeiro to make his observations, but, not having time to learn Dutch or Portuguese, he plumped for St. Helena: the southern-most outpost of British rule.

Although discovered by the Portuguese, the island had been in the possession of the East India Company for the last 25 years. Now the company found itself prevailed upon by King Charles II to grant free passage there to Halley and his companion. 'We, being graciously willing', wrote the King, responding to Halley's request, 'to give all encouragement and protection to whatever may tend to the improvement of navigation and be beneficial to the public, have thought fit hereby most particularly to recommend him to you, that you will give order, that he, his friend and their necessaries may be transported to the said island [St.Helena] upon the first of your ships that shall go thither, and that he be received and entertained there and have such assistance and countenance from your officers as he may stand in need of.' The company was advised that the purpose of the expedition was to 'make observations for rectifying and finishing the celestial globe.' [3] Every assistance was to be given to the pair in what, after all, was 'so useful an undertaking.' The company duly co-operated—it didn't have much choice—and urged its employees to treat young Halley and his friend 'with all civilitie'.

After a voyage lasting three months, they arrived within sight of the spectacular coastline of St. Helena. The forbidding cliffs, towering 300 metres and more above the heaving Atlantic swell, allowed few landing places. The *Unity* skirted along the north coast and finally pulled into the port of Jamestown. This was the principal settlement: home of most of the 300 or so inhabitants, including no less than 80 black slaves. Here, the two friends would stay for more than a year.

The sojourn on the island proved acutely frustrating. The Governor of the island, Gregory Field, turned out to be a singularly discourteous host. But worse than that, the weather was appalling. Although Halley had been assured by acquaintances from the West Indies that the skies above St. Helena would be clear, in the event they turned out to be unusually cloudy. 'Such hath been my ill fortune,' he lamented to his patron Sir Jonas Moore, the Surveyor-General of the Ordnance, 'that the Horizon of this Island is almost covered with a Cloud, which sometimes for some weeks together hath hid the stars from us.' [4] Hardly ever did clear skies persist for more than an hour at a time. His observing

Edmond Halley *(By permission of the President and Council of the Royal Society)*

program was subject to constant disruption. Nevertheless, he persevered and, during his year on St. Helena, he compiled a catalogue of 341 stars, which was hailed as a great success on his return to England. Flamsteed even went so far as to call him 'the Southern Tycho'.

Robert Hooke (1635–1703) presented Halley's planisphere and description of the Southern Hemisphere stars to the Royal Society in the November of

1768. The Society was so impressed, that it ordered copies to be sent to a number of foreign astronomers at its own expense. Charles II was also impressed: not least with the new constellation—Robur Carolina (Charles's Oak), named in his honour—depicted on the planisphere. He recommended to Oxford University that it confer a Master of Arts degree on Halley. This was duly done. The Royal Society two weeks later elected him as a Fellow.

During the stay on the island, Halley observed a transit of Mercury. This single observation, on 7th November 1677, was possibly one of the most important in the history of astronomy, for it started ideas racing through his mind, which would have repercussions across the centuries.

He had been afflicted by a multitude of adverse circumstances, but the transit of Mercury was a wonderful exception. None of the tables possessed by Halley was accurate enough to guarantee that the transit would occur when the Sun was above the horizon. Furthermore, the night before the transit was windy and cloudy and the clouds persisted into the day. Despite this unpropitious start, with his telescope set up and trained on the Sun, Halley waited patiently. The total duration of the transit was 5 hours, 14 minutes and 20 seconds and for a full three and a half hours of this time, Mercury remained obscured by cloud. Nevertheless, in clear intervals, fortuitously timed, he managed to see both the ingress and egress of Mercury.

'I happened to observe with the utmost care, Mercury passing over the Sun's disk,' he reported, 'and contrary to expectation, I very accurately obtained, with a good 24-foot telescope, the very moment in which Mercury, entering the Sun's limb, seemed to touch it internally...forming an angle of internal contact. Hence I discovered the precise quantity of time the whole body of Mercury had then appeared within the Sun's disk, and that without an error of one single second of time...On observing this I immediately concluded, that the Sun's parallax might be...determined by such observations...'[5]

Halley had realised that, if the transit were to be observed from different latitudes, then the parallax effect would cause the observers to see Mercury going onto the Sun's disc, and subsequently leaving it, at quite different times. More importantly, analysis of the time differences might reveal the distance of the Sun.

He was not the first person to see this potential. In 1663, the young Scottish mathematician, James Gregory (1638–1675), had suggested, in his work *Optica Promota* (1663), that transits, if observed from different places, of known latitude, might serve to allow the distance of the Sun to be determined. It is quite possible that Halley was aware of Gregory's proposal. In any event, as a result of seeing the transit of Mercury, it was he who developed the idea into a practical method and exhorted others to apply it in a concerted effort.

He hoped that comparison of his own measurements on St. Helena with similar ones in the northern hemisphere would bear fruit. Full of optimism, he wrote to Sir Jonas Moore: 'I have…had the opportunity of observing the ingress and egress of [Mercury] on the [Sun], which compared with the like observation made in England, will give a demonstration of the Sun's Parallax, which hitherto was never proved, but by probable arguments.' [6]

He was to be mightily disappointed. Clouds covered all the sites in England from where observations might have been made. At Avignon, in France, Jean Charles Gallet, the Provost of the Church of St Symphorean, briefly saw Mercury on the Sun, but only at egress. Of this effort moreover, Flamsteed unkindly remarked: 'I find little sound and could wish some more intelligent person had had that opportunity.' [7]

As it happens, even if comparable observations had been made in England or France, Halley would have found it difficult to extract any reliable result. In principle, the idea was sound, but the available means of measurement were far too crude. It could have worked, he later explained, 'provided Mercury were but nearer to the Earth, and had a greater parallax from the Sun…' As things stood however, 'Mercury, though frequently to be seen on the Sun, is not to be looked upon as fit for our purpose.'

'There remains then,' added Halley, 'the transit of Venus over the Sun's disc.' [8]

The parallax effect would be much greater for Venus than for Mercury, because of the greater closeness of Venus to the Earth. The corresponding difference in timings would therefore be greater. Halley returned to this theme over the succeeding years in a number of papers submitted to the Royal Society. 'This sight,' he said, referring to the transit of Venus, 'which is by far the noblest astronomy affords, like the secular games*, is denied to mortals for a whole century, by the strict laws of motion. It will be…shown, that by this observation alone, the distance of the Sun, from the Earth, might be determined with the greatest certainty…' [9]

What Halley had in mind was essentially a simple method, based on simple effects. His reasoning went along the following lines:

Venus overtakes the Earth, on the 'inside track', in its orbit around the Sun. It passes between the Earth and the Sun. At this stage in its orbit, it appears to be moving at 4 arc-minutes in every hour, relative to the centre of the Earth. We needn't consider the speed of the Earth along its own orbit, because 4 minutes per hour is the *relative* speed of Venus: that is, how fast Venus appears to be moving past the Sun. If, during a transit of Venus, the Earth could be persuaded to stop spinning on its axis, whilst we admired the progress of Venus, the silhouette of the planet would seem to move across the Sun's disc at this rate.

The Sun measures approximately half a degree in the sky. Therefore, if the transit of Venus were more or less across the centre of the Sun's disc, it would complete the crossing in about seven and a half hours. Assuming that the nodes of Venus' orbit would remain where they were when Horrocks made his sighting in 1639, Halley calculated that the next transit of Venus would actually be some distance below the Sun's centre. Its path would therefore be shorter. He reckoned that the duration of the transit, seen from a non-rotating Earth, would be about 7 hours 20 minutes.

Now, if we consider how things will appear to a real observer, on the surface a spinning Earth, we will see that the timings will be somewhat different.

Firstly, an observer in the west will see the commencement of the transit later than an observer in the east. Secondly, a crucial difference arises from the fact that our observer is being whirled around the Earth's axis once every 24 hours. And the whirling motion—from west to east—is in precisely the opposite direction to that of Venus as it passes across the Sun. The effect of this contrary motion will be to make Venus appear to go faster. Anyone who has looked out of a train window, as the train pulls out of a station, will be familiar with this effect. The motion of the train appears to impart an

* The Secular Games in Ancient Rome were only celebrated once in a century

opposite motion to anything outside the window. If another train is moving past in the opposite direction, it appears to be given an additional speed.

In the time taken up by the transit of Venus, our observer will have spun more than one quarter of the way around the Earth's axis. The distance traveled in this spin will depend, of course, on the latitude: the nearer the observer is to the Equator, the greater will be the distance traveled, the greater the speed imparted by the spin and the faster Venus will appear to progress in its journey across the Sun. But, if the observer is at the North Pole, no distance will be traveled. This shivering soul will simply turn around on the spot, as it were. In this case Venus will not appear to be speeded up.

A fairground analogy might help us to visualise the phenomenon more readily. Imagine a carousel, or merry-go-round, and, some distance away, a tent. The tent can represent the Sun and the carousel represents the Earth, spinning, as it does, about an axis at its centre. As we look down on the carousel we note that the spin is anticlockwise. On the carousel, a fairground attendant stands at the centre, looking thoroughly bored. She has to do this job all day long, so we cannot expect her to get the same thrill as all the merry, screaming children who surround her. The children are sitting astride the wooden horses which are positioned at the outer edge of the carousel. The horses are being carried around the carousel at a fair old speed. Not fast enough to make the children fly off, but easily enough to make them giddy and ever so slightly dizzy as the fairground whirls past. It wouldn't do for the attendant to get dizzy, so she has a stationary platform at the centre.

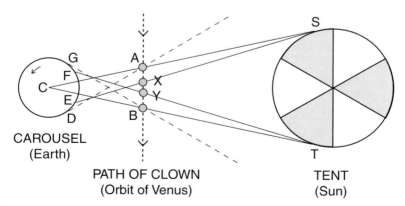

Fairground analogy showing the parallax effect from a spinning Earth

All of a sudden, the attendant spies a clown on stilts, aiming for the gap between the carousel and the tent. Walking neither towards the carousel nor the tent, the clown keeps up a constant pace and passes, in a straight line, between the two: nearer to the carousel than to the tent. As the clown progresses, the attendant sees behind him, first the left-hand side of the tent at S, and then, a few seconds later, the right-hand side of it at T. In the diagram above, the positions of the clown at these two moments are shown by points A and B, respectively, and the position of the attendant is C.

Let's see now what is happening through the eyes of a child sitting on one of the carousel horses. The child is at D when the attendant thinks the clown is in front of the left-hand side of the tent: that is, when the clown is at A. At this moment, however, the child thinks that the clown has got quite a distance to go before passing in front of the tent. Such is the speed of the carousel, that the child has reached point E, before seeing the tent behind the clown, and the clown is then at X. By the time the attendant sees the clown at B, the child on the horse has moved to G and thinks that the clown has already gone past the tent. It was when she was at point F and the clown was at Y that the clown was in line with the right-hand side of the tent, so far as the child was concerned.

Thus, to the attendant, the clown was in front of the tent while walking from A to B, but, to the child spinning around the carousel, this only happened between X and Y—a noticeably shorter time.

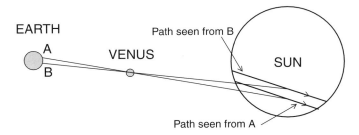

In just the same way, the duration of the passage of Venus in front of the Sun is dependent on where we are positioned on a spinning Earth. This is the parallax effect at work. To Halley, it suggested an obvious method of finding out the distance of both Venus and the Sun.

The observer's latitude affects the duration of a transit in two ways. Firstly, it changes the apparent speed of Venus, as explained above by our fairground analogy—the diameter of the circle of latitude being as the diameter of the carousel. Secondly, it affects the length of path across the Sun, which the planet appears to follow. The further south the observer is on the Earth, the further north on the Sun's disc Venus will appear to be. Thus, the length of path will be different and the duration will change correspondingly. This also is a parallax effect.

From the difference in the duration of the transit, as seen from varying sites, the difference between the parallaxes of Venus and the Sun can be obtained. The parallax of the Sun, it will be recalled, is the apparent angular size of the Earth's radius, seen from the Sun. Similarly, the parallax of Venus is the apparent angular size of the Earth's radius, seen from Venus.

At first sight, it might be thought that knowing merely the *difference* between these two parallaxes would leave us no nearer knowing the actual parallax of the Sun. This is where Kepler's Laws come to our assistance.

Thanks to the Third Law, Halley and his successors were able to know, to a high degree of precision, the ratio of the distances of Venus from the Earth and Venus from the Sun. If at the time of the 1761 transit this ratio was two-fifths, then simple maths dictates that the difference in parallaxes, multiplied by this ratio, gives the parallax of the Sun. The radius of the Earth, divided by the solar parallax (expressed in radians) will then give the distance of the Sun.

In short, the parallax effect, Halley anticipated, would bring about 'very sensible differences between the times in which Venus will seem to be passing over the Sun at different parts of the Earth.' 'From these differences, if they be observed as they ought,' he explained, 'the Sun's parallax may be determined even to a small part of a second. Nor do we require any other instruments for this purpose, than common telescopes and clocks, only good of their kind; and in the observers, nothing more is needed than fidelity, diligence, and a moderate skill in Astronomy. For there is no need that the latitude of the place should be scrupulously observed, nor that the hours themselves should be accurately determined with respect to the meridian: it is sufficient that the clocks be regulated according to the motion of the heavens, if the times be well reckoned from the total ingress of Venus into the Sun's disc, to the beginning of her egress from it; that is, when the dark globe of Venus first begins to touch the bright limb of the Sun within; which moments, I know by my own experience, may be observed to within a second of time.' [10]

Vital to Halley's method was an accurate size for the Earth. After all, the Earth, in effect, was to be the baseline for a grandiose triangulation of Venus. Fortunately, the century which saw Halley's mapping of the southern skies, also saw the first real improvements on the values found for the Earth's diameter by the ancient Greek and Arab investigators.

One such improvement was due to Richard Norwood (1590?–1675), an apprentice fish-monger, who ran away to sea, to learn the 'art of navigation', and came back a teacher of mathematics. In 1635, on the longest day of the year, the inhabitants of York, in northern England, must have been puzzled to see that Norwood had stationed himself in the middle of their city, equipped with an enormous sextant—more than five feet in radius. What he said to any curious on-lookers is not recorded. If he had told them the truth, that he was measuring the Earth, he probably would not have been believed. As the Sun reached its noon-time high point, he measured its elevation as carefully as he could. He found it to be 59°33'. This was a repetition of a measurement which he had carried out two years earlier, also on the longest day, somewhere near the Tower of London. In London he had found the elevation of the Sun to be 62°1'. The difference between the two figures, 2°28', was brought about by, and was exactly equivalent to, the difference in latitude between the two places. Armed with this knowledge, he then moved on to the arduous task of measuring the north-south distance between London and York.

Making his way along the high road, following its every twist and turn, he gauged the distance traversed. Mostly he did it with a chain, 99 feet in length, but sometimes he simply paced the distances. Every change of direction was scrupulously surveyed, using a circumferentor, a fore-runner of the theodolite. Due allowances were also made for the elongating effect of hills and dales upon his route.

Once recovered from the exhausting journey, he set about the analysis of his survey. His conclusion was that the observing station in York was exactly 9149 chains, or 171½ miles, north of that in London. This implied that one degree of latitude was equivalent to about 69½ miles in the north-south direction. Consequently, the distance for 360 degrees, the entire circumference of the globe, could be calculated, and, from this, the radius. Norwood found the radius of the Earth to be 3,983 miles and, in 1636, published his findings in a little book, entitled *The Seaman's Practice*.

Norwood's approach was basically an updated version of the famous method of Eratosthenes in ancient times. The difference in the altitude of the Sun, seen from two places, at the Summer Solstice, was the basis of both attempts. The distance measured in the 1630's was perhaps more accurate, but no one can really be sure how Eratosthenes made his survey or what the value of his unit, the stade, was in modern units.

Given the simplicity of his technique, Richard Norwood's 3,983 miles compares surprisingly well with the modern value of 3,963 miles for the radius at the Equator. The Sun is a rather large object in the sky and it cannot have been a simple task for him to measure the true elevation of its centre. The distance measurement along the highway between London and York was also somewhat flawed, to say the least. Nevertheless, this was a noble attempt to get the measure of the Earth.

Of an entirely different order of exactitude, was the celebrated survey of the Frenchman, Jean Picard (1620–1682), in 1669.

Picard commenced by measuring, very precisely, a straight line between the mill at Villejuif and the flagpole at Ivoisey, along the road between Paris and Fontainebleau. This line, 5,663 toise, or 11,037 metres, long, was set out using a 4 toise (7.796 metres) measuring rod, formed by pikes screwed to each other, end-to-end. This was to be the base of a large triangle which he then set out, across the adjacent countryside, using a 38 inch radius quadrant, furnished with telescopic sights. When he was satisfied with this triangle, he then set out a further large triangle, using another side of the first triangle as the base of the second. In this manner, he set out a whole string of triangles, stretching from Malvoisine in the south, to the cathedral lantern of Notre Dame, at Amiens, in the north - a distance of about 96 miles (155 km) in the north-south direction: that is, along the meridian through Malvoisine or Amiens. With this distance now fixed, his next job was 'to enquire what answers to it in the heavens?' [11] He measured the difference in the latitudes of the two places by checking the difference in the altitude of a star in the constellation Cassiopeia (δ), when viewed from each place. A star

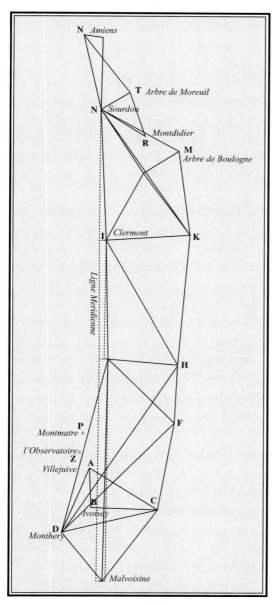

Picard's meridian line triangulation

has no perceptible size, so this method of measuring latitudes was capable of giving much more precision than methods involving the Sun. He concluded that one degree of latitude was equivalent to about 69 miles and that the radius of the Earth was 3,955 miles (6365.6 kilometres).

National prestige was a powerful motivation in seventeenth century science. When the English King, Charles II, heard about Jean Picard's measurement of one degree of latitude, he let it be known that he would like the Royal Society to organise a similar measurement in England. Not that he offered to make a financial contribution towards such a venture! The Royal Society itself was in no position to put up the necessary funding and so the idea was discretely put on hold. But, in July 1686, the proposal re-surfaced and the Council of the Society ordered 'that the treasurer, to encourage the measuring of a degree of the Earth, do give to Mr.Halley fifty pounds or fifty copies of the History of Fishes when he shall have measured a degree to the satisfaction of Sir Christopher Wren, the president, and Sir John Hoskyns.' [12]

Halley probably groaned inwardly as he saw the *History of Fishes* mentioned in the offer. The Royal Society had nearly bankrupted itself by paying for the publication of this book. Written by Francis Willoughby and John Ray, it was lavishly illustrated and was very expensive. The Society was left with numerous unsold copies. The result was that the Society had to pay the £50 annual salary of Halley, who at that time was its clerk, entirely in copies of the *History of Fishes*! He must have been heartily sick of the sight of the book.

Nothing came of the plan to have Halley measure a degree of latitude. He did try, but was defeated by factors which show how parochial life was for ordinary folk in seventeenth century England. In November 1686, he reported: 'I attempted about the end of last August to make a survey of a degree of the Earth, by a scale of Triangles; but found severall obstacles that obliged me to desist. The chief whereof were that I found a great and insuperable difficulty to come to the objects that I had seen at a great distance, for the country people I observed could tell me nothing of places above 7 or 8 miles off: And that at about 20 miles North from London, the country is very thick of high Woods, and the hills so near of a hight, that there were no conspicuus objects to be found: so that I saw an absolute necessity of making a preparative perambulation, to find out the eminent Objects so that I might not be at a Loss upon my second attempt.' [13]

There was no 'second attempt'. Other priorities intervened. The triangulation of England had to wait until the Jacobite rebellion of 1745 had given a military incentive for a network of triangles to be established between signal stations on prominent hills throughout the land.

Meanwhile, Halley's interest in the 'triangulation' of Venus continued to intensify. In 1691 he wrote a lengthy account of the significance of future transits of Venus. He knew that he himself would not live to see one: no more would occur until the May (old-style calendar) of 1761 and 1769. 'In the month of May', he pointed out, 'Venus has not hitherto been seen by any mortal within the Sun; but from my calculations it appears, that Venus for the next time will enter the Sun 1761, May, 25d 17h 55m* [old-style]'. [14] In a paper which he gave to the Royal Society in 1716, aged almost sixty, he appealed directly to future generations of astronomers: 'I recommend it, therefore, again and again, to those curious Astronomers, who (when I am dead) will have an opportunity of observing these things, that they would remember this my admonition, and diligently apply themselves with all their might to the making of this observation; and I earnestly wish them all imaginable success; in the first place that they may not, by the unseasonable obscurity of a cloudy sky, be deprived of this most desirable sight; and then, that having ascertained with more exactness the magnitudes of the planetary orbits, it may redound to their eternal fame and glory' [15]

His appeal was not confined to general principles. Halley, the thoroughly practical astronomer, pinpointed specific locations that might be most convenient for effectual observations. Of prime importance would be the Tropics—say the Bay of Bengal, in the East Indies—where he expected that the middle of the transit would take place at noon, and the North American Arctic regions—say Port Nelson, in Hudson's Bay—where mid-transit would be at midnight.

'If it should happen,' he wrote, 'that this transit should be properly observed by skilful persons at both these places, it is clear, that its duration will be 17 minutes longer, as seen from Port Nelson, than as seen from the East Indies. Nor is it of much consequence (if the English shall at that time give any attention to this affair) whether the observation be made at Fort-George, commonly called Madras, or at Bencoolen on the western shore of the island of Sumatra, near the Equator. But if the French should be disposed to take any pains herein, an observer may station himself conveniently enough at Pondicherry on the west shore of the bay of Bengal, where the altitude of the pole is about 12 degrees. As to the Dutch, their celebrated mart at Batavia will afford them a place of observation fit enough for this purpose, provided they also have but a disposition to assist in advancing, in this particular, the knowledge of the heavens.

'And indeed I could wish that many observations of the same phenomenon might be taken by different persons at several places, both that we might

---

* Making allowance for prevailing methods of astronomical time-reckoning, this was equivalent to 5h 55m in the morning of 26th May (6th June in the new-style calendar).

arrive at a greater degree of certainty by their agreement, and also lest any single observer should be deprived, by the intervention of clouds, of a sight, which I know not whether any man living in this or the next age will ever see again; and on which depends the certain and adequate solution of a problem the most noble, and at any other time not to be attained to.' [16]

As a consequence of this attention to detail, the scientific communities of the world were given more than four decades to accustom themselves to the grandiose scale of the plan envisioned by Halley.

He prophesied that his paper would be 'immortal', and indeed it was. His exhortations and detailed plans, projected beyond the grave, caused well-equipped expeditions to set out to far flung corners of the Earth to observe the 1761 and 1769 transits. The prize, if all went well, would be nothing less than the solar parallax and, therefore, the true distance of the Sun.

Edmond Halley died peacefully, on 14th January 1742 (new-style calendar), at the age of eighty-five. His tomb is at St. Margaret's in Blackheath. The tombstone however, was removed to the Royal Observatory in Greenwich in 1854, where it can still be seen today. It bears the inscription: 'Quietly under this marble, Edmond Halley, LL.D., easily the prince of astronomers of his age, rests with his dearest wife. Reader, to know how truly great that man was, read his many writings; wherein he illustrated, improved, and enlarged almost all the arts and sciences. It is just therefore that as in life he was highly honoured by his fellow citizens, so his memory should be gratefully respected by posterity. Born 1656, died 1741. His two daughters most dutifully consecrated this stone to the best of parents.' [17]

CHAPTER 11

THE 1761 TRANSIT OF VENUS

As the predicted 6th June 1761 transit of Venus approached, interest was enormous. Halley's entreaties had not been in vain. In every country that prided itself on scientific achievement, preparations were made for what became a great international venture.

Interest was nowhere greater than in France. The French astronomer, Joseph-Nicolas Delisle (1688–1768), had devoted a great deal of time to studying the problem of how to determine the solar parallax. He devised a simpler variant of Halley's plan. In Delisle's method it would not be necessary for a given observer to view both the ingress and egress of Venus. Either one would suffice. Provided that each observer's exact position on the Earth's surface was known, the method would succeed. This had substantial advantages, since it opened up the possibility of more observing sites being useful. Sites that would only see the beginning or end of the transit could be utilised. Even at locations where the whole transit would be seen, there would be less chance of cloud wrecking the observations.

Joseph-Nicolas Delisle *(Courtesy of the Observatoire de Paris)*

Delisle had visited Halley in England in 1724. Such was Halley's respect for the French astronomer that he gave Delisle a copy of his unpublished

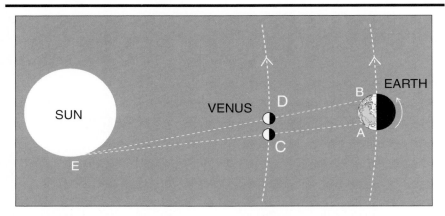

In Delisle's method only the ingress or egress needed timing, provided that the precise locations of A and B were known. At B Venus will appear to enter the Sun's disk later than at A.

astronomical tables. These became available to other astronomers only in 1749, seven years after Halley's death. Delisle used them to refine Halley's transit predictions. He also made important corrections to the tables. At the end of April 1760, thirteen months before the transit was due, he presented recommendations and an accompanying map of the world, or *mappemonde*, to the Académie des Sciences. The mappemonde showed the zones of visibility for the transit. With this tool observing stations could be chosen to best effect.

Under the auspices of the Académie, prominent astronomers made preparations to sail to far-away destinations. Long-distance travel and sea faring in the mid-eighteenth century were occupations only for hardy souls. Even so, these eager emissaries of Science cannot have realised how dear would be the personal cost of the voyages to see Venus upon the face of the Sun. At least one would eventually pay with his life. The sailors transporting them, although accustomed to the mortal risks of war, cannot have imagined how many of their number also would lose their lives in so peaceful a venture.

Amongst the most illustrious of those about to embark were: Guillaume-Joseph-Hyacinthe-Jean-Baptiste Le Gentil (1725–1792), going to Pondichery, India; Alexandre-Gui Pingré (1711–1796), aiming for the Isle of Rodrigué in the Indian Ocean; and, Jean-Baptiste Chappe d'Auteroche (1728–1769), bound for Siberia.

At the other side of the English Channel, British preparations were slower in getting under way, but, once started, were no less thorough.

Remarkably, exchange of ideas between the French and British astronomers continued to take place, even though France and Britain were embroiled in the Seven Years' War (1756–1763). Delisle's recommendations and *mappemonde* were presented to the members of the Royal Society in London.

The minutes of the Royal Society Council meeting of 26th June 1760 record, with a striking lack of elaboration, and almost algebraic generality, that a discussion took place on the sending of 'proper persons to proper places, to observe the approaching Transit of Venus…the Several Instruments that will be necessary for the work; and the Expenses which will be likely to attend it.' [1]

Delisle's Mappemonde of the 1761 transit of Venus
(Woolf, Harry; The Transits of Venus, copyright © 1959 by PUP.
Reprinted by permission of Princeton University Press)

Work proceeded immediately on choosing appropriate observing stations. Sites were selected partly from Halley's list and partly from Delisle's mappemonde. They included St.Helena, in the South Atlantic, and Bencoolen, on Sumatra in the East Indies.

The Society petitioned for funding by submitting a Memorial to the Treasury. A forthright appeal to national honour was included. Maybe this was a real motivation, partly born out of the on-going war with France. Or, maybe, this was calculated to be the best way to extract government support. Lord Macclesfield, President of the Society, explained that 'the Motives…are the Improvement of Astronomy and the Honour of this Nation; which seems to be more particularly concerned in the exact observation of this rare phaenomenon, that was never observed but by one Englishman…and …pointed out and illustrated by Dr.Halley another Englishman. And it might afford too just ground to Foreigners for reproaching this Nation in general (not inferior to any other in every branch of learning and more especially in Astronome); if, while the French King is sending observers…not only to Pondicherie and the Cape of Good Hope, but also to the Northern Parts of Siberia; and the Court of Russia are doing the same to the most Eastern Confines of the Greater Tartary; not to mention the several Observers who are going to various Places, on the same errand from different parts of Europe; England should neglect to send Observers to such places…subject to the Crown of Great Britain.' The honour of the Royal Society was also at stake and the Society, Macclesfield affirmed, was 'desirous of satisfying the universal Expectations of the World in this respect'. [2]

It was resolved that Nevil Maskelyne (1732–1811) and Robert Waddington would go to St.Helena to observe the transit. Charles Mason (1730–1787), assistant to the Astronomer Royal, together with an amateur from Durham, Jeremiah Dixon (1733–1779), would go to Bencoolen.

In the run-up to the departure of the expeditions, the Society discussed and re-discussed the precise circumstances of the transit. How would the event appear to observers at different locations? How would the timings vary? Delisle's mappemonde had started the ball rolling, but now there was no shortage of 'home-grown' commentaries to keep up the momentum.

Of the papers on the topic, few would have been as clearly explained as that presented to the Society in November 1760 by the self-taught Scottish astronomer, James Ferguson (1710–1776). The presentation was illustrated with several of the carefully delineated geometrical projections for which Ferguson was justly acquiring a reputation. Soon afterwards, a version of the paper was published in pamphlet form under the title: *A Plain Method of Determining the Parallax of Venus by her Transit over the Sun.*

Rarely was there such a contrast between audience and speaker. Almost all the Fellows of the Royal Society had academic degrees or titles. Ferguson however—aptly nicknamed 'The Peasant-boy Philosopher'—had had only three months' formal education in his entire life. Born into a poor family in Banffshire in 1710, he had spent his youth as a shepherd and a farm labourer. Despite this disadvantaged start, by dint of his own efforts and timely assistance from well-disposed patrons, he managed to become one of the most popular astronomical authors in the land. He had a gift for lucid explanation, in non-mathematical language, and his explanatory drawings were models of clarity. More than a few of his audience—learned or not—must have been grateful that Ferguson was on hand to digest the complex technical issues and represent them with his exquisite drawings. Although Halley's method was based on a simple principle, the three-dimensional geometry involved in its practical application was enough to challenge anyone.

The expedition to Bencoolen was the first to depart, in January 1761. Before Mason and Dixon set sail out of Portsmouth on board *HMS Seahorse* though, the Admiralty took the precaution of writing to the Royal Society to ask for a suitable alternative site in the East Indies, 'in case the Seahorse when she arrives there should find Bencoolen in the hands of the French'. [3]

Batavia (present day Jakarta, in Indonesia) was nominated as the fallback site. This timely reminder of the war was not misplaced. Whilst still in the English Channel, the Seahorse was involved in a serious battle with the French frigate, *le Grand*. Extensively damaged and with eleven dead and thirty-seven wounded, the Seahorse was obliged to turn about and make for Plymouth. The Admiralty gave orders for the Seahorse to be repaired. It also arranged that a seventy-gun ship would escort her out of the Channel upon completion of the repairs.

Mason wrote to the Royal Society asking for new instructions, since he thought it would now be impossible to get to Bencoolen on time. Within two weeks, not having received a supportive reply, he wrote again—this time defiantly informing the Society that he and Dixon would not go to Bencoolen: 'We will not proceed thither, let the consequence be what it will.' [4] He proposed that, instead, they should go to Scanderoon in the eastern Black Sea. Dixon also wrote, though in more conciliatory terms, with much the same message.

To say that Mason and Dixon's letters met with an unsympathetic response, would be a gross understatement. The 31st January 1761 Council meeting of the Royal Society must have been a very bitter gathering. The recent peril in which the lives of its astronomers had been placed in no way diminished the Society's wrath at the whiff of rebellion.

A ringing denunciation of Mason and Dixon was unanimously agreed: '…their refusal to proceed upon this voyage, after having so publickly and notoriously ingaged in it…[would] be a reproach to the Nation in general, and to the Royal Society in particular, and more Especially and fatally to themselves.' Just in case these words made no impression on the pair, the Council went on to say that it would pursue them with 'the most inflexible Resentment' and prosecute them with 'the utmost severity of the Law'. Somewhat incongruously associated with this harsh threat was a postscript leaving it 'to the discretion of the Observers when they are upon their Voyage, to act in the best Manner, for Effectually answering the ends of their designation'. [5]

The effect was immediate. The Society's 'dutiful servants' upped anchor at the beginning of February, bound for Bencoolen. They never arrived. Bencoolen, it transpired, had been taken by the French, even before the Seahorse had first put out from Portsmouth!

Mason and Dixon landed at Cape Town, South Africa, on 27th April 1761 and wrote to the Royal Society that they were preparing to observe the transit from there. Batavia, the original alternative to Bencoolen, was some six thousand miles further away and, with only six weeks left to the transit, it seemed by now to be an unrealistic destination.

At the time, Cape Town was a Dutch colony and Mason and Dixon asked their Dutch hosts to provide a suitable site and materials for the erection of an observatory. These requests were fully complied with. The astronomers had been given very detailed instructions by the Astronomer Royal, James Bradley (1693-1762), on how to proceed:

Locate the observatory where there is a clear view toward the northeast, north and northwest. Observe the first and second contacts of Venus with the limb of the Sun. Then measure the distance of Venus from the limb of the Sun to ascertain the nearest approach of Venus to the centre of the Sun's disk. Measure the diameter of Venus.

Set up the clock so that the observers at the telescopes are immediately accessible to it. Observers must be careful not to prejudice one another in their judgements of events and times. Make a preliminary trial of the clock with its pendulum adjusted as it was at Greenwich to ascertain how much it loses in a sidereal day. Then adjust it to solar time. Keep a record of the temperature in the clock case. Record how much the pendulum must be changed in length to keep solar time... [6]

These instructions were meticulously carried out. A circular observatory, about four metres in diameter, with a conical, moveable roof was built. Mason and Dixon then set about making the various observations that would allow the latitude and longitude of the site to be determined. The clock's timekeeping was tested against the nightly passage of the bright star Procyon across the meridian—that is, the imaginary north-south line in the sky above their observing station. The location of their meridian had been arrived at by repeated observation of the stars Antares and Altair. For each star, a pair of times was noted: first, when the star was at a given altitude above the eastern horizon; second, when the star had moved across, during the night, to an exactly equal altitude above the western horizon. At a time precisely mid-way between these two sightings, the star would be exactly on the north-south line.

The latitude and longitude of the Cape Town observatory were determined with a high degree of accuracy. 'The situation of few places is better determined', Maskelyne wrote in the first issue of the *Nautical Almanac* (1767).

The day of the transit arrived. At the first glimmer of dawn Mason and Dixon were ready and waiting. The Sun ascended above the horizon—its form shimmering in a thick haze. To their dismay, it quickly disappeared behind clouds. It was 20 minutes before they caught their first sight of Venus on the Sun's disc. 'When I saw the planet first, its periphery and that of the Sun were in a great tremor,' reported Mason, 'but this vanished as the Sun rose and became well defined'. [7]

Conscientiously, mustering all the precision of which their instruments were capable, the astronomers proceeded to monitor every aspect of the long-awaited spectacle. They were determined to render a good account of themselves. No measurement that might be of service was omitted. At several stages during the transit, the apparent distance of Venus from the Sun's outer edge, or limb, was measured. The relative sizes of Venus and the Sun were noted and the times of the internal and external contact at egress were recorded. As instructed, great care was taken to operate independently of each other in the matter of timing.

Although Mason and Dixon observed from the same site, their timings for the moment of internal contact at egress were surprisingly different, by a full four seconds. This brought to light a difficulty, which was to affect many of the transit observations, to a greater or lesser degree. Whereas Halley had reported timing the internal contact of Mercury, during his stay on St.Helena, 'without an error of one single second of time', this did not seem to be possible with Venus: unexpected problems occurred. For most observers, the main problem was the *black drop* effect, which occurred at both ingress and egress.

At ingress, as Venus approached internal contact, something strange seemed to happen: rather than separating cleanly from the Sun's limb, the silhouetted black circle of Venus appeared to stick to the edge of the Sun and became locally stretched. The appearance was somewhat like a droplet of water elongating before detaching itself from a leaking pipe. After being stretched out in this manner, the silhouette of Venus then suddenly snapped free from

The 'black drop' effect

the Sun's limb, revealing that it was already some way into its path across the Sun. Thus, the precise moment of internal contact was unclear. At egress, the process was reversed.

The black-drop effect was later put down to a combination of factors, including atmospheric disturbance, imperfections of the eye, instrumental deficiency and irradiation—the same phenomenon which makes the setting Sun appear to take a bite out of the horizon. When a dark object (in this case the silhouette of Venus) is set against an exceptionally bright background, the light from the background appears to encroach upon the dark object and make it seem smaller.

The black-drop was not the only complication. For some observers the entire disc of the planet Venus announced its presence almost as soon as the first contact with the limb of the Sun. Its silhouette could be clearly seen, surrounded by a ghostly halo of light. This—the 'luminous ring' effect— was the first evidence that Venus has an atmosphere, through which the sunlight was being bent, or refracted. The planet Mercury does not have an atmosphere and therefore its transit was not attended by this problem to the same degree.

Mason and Dixon's observations at the Cape turned out to be the only ones available for the South Atlantic, since Maskelyne and Waddington's observations from St.Helena had been completely ruined. 'From the very cloudy weather, which prevailed here for the whole month preceding the transit,' wrote Maskelyne to the Earl of Macclesfield, 'I, indeed, almost despaired of obtaining any sight of it at all. I was, however, fortunate enough to obtain two fair views, though but of short continuance, of this curious celestial phaenomenon. The first was a few minutes after sun-rise, when I was surprized not only at seeing Venus so very large, but also much nearer the sun's limb, than I had reason to expect from the best grounded calculations; …' and [later] '…after I had measured the distance of Venus from the sun's limb, the clouds returned again, and prevented me, not only from making any more observations of the same kind, or measuring Venus's diameter, but also, what was of much more consequence, from observing the last internal contact of Venus from the sun's limb, which was the principal observation of all.' [8]

*****

When the French astronomer, Le Gentil, sailed out of the harbour at Brest on 26th March 1760, bound for Pondichery in India, he was in his late thirties. Like his British counterparts, he too was on board a warship: the fifty-gun *le Berryer*. This was a far cry from the life he had originally planned. He had been attracted to a career in the Church, until hearing Delisle lecture at the Collège Royal awakened his interest in astronomy. He soon had a job working at the Royal Observatory under Cassini de Thury and in 1753 participated in observing a transit of Mercury. By the time of the voyage to the French colony at Pondichery, he was already a respected member of the Académie.

After almost four months at sea, Le Gentil arrived at the Île de France (now known as Mauritius), to the east of Madagascar. Apart from pursuit by the British Navy, near the Cape of Good Hope, no serious problem had been encountered thus far. It was upon debarkation at the Île de France that his luck started to drain away. He learned that Pondichery—still two and a half thousand miles away—was surrounded by the British: besieged by land and blockaded by sea. A French fleet, which had been preparing to raise the siege, had been irreparably damaged on coral reefs as a result of a sudden hurricane. Many lives were lost.

There was now little chance of getting to Pondichery in time for the 6th June. In February, Le Gentil informed the Académie that he was thinking of going to Batavia instead. Within a week he had changed his mind and resolved that, should no other option present itself within two months, he would go to the Isle of Rodrigué. He didn't need to wait long. Orders arriving from France urged that troops be sent to Pondichery. He decided to chance his luck with them. On 16th March he embarked on the troopship *la Sylphide*, thinking that even if Pondichery was still blockaded by the enemy, there would be other suitable, neutral, places *en route*.

Alas for Le Gentil, *la Sylphide* was delayed by terrible storms and on 20th May he learned that the British had already captured Pondichery. The ship turned around and made haste back towards the Île de France. Thus, it was from the rolling deck of the ship that Le Gentil disconsolately gazed at the Sun in a clear blue sky, on the 6th June. The transit was in progress and he was unable to make any worthwhile measurement.

He resolved to stay on in the area for another year, in order to study the geography and natural history. At least then, his long voyage would have had some purpose. During the course of his stay, he made a bold decision. In order to avoid missing the next transit of Venus in 1769, he would stay on for eight years!

Bust of Alexandre-Gui Pingré by J-J Caffiéri (© *Bibliothèque Sainte-Geneviève, Paris*)

Alexandre-Gui Pingré, by contrast, *did* manage to see the transit. But the mishaps besetting him were no less daunting.

The Académie des Sciences had written to the British Admiralty asking for 'safe and uninterrupted' passage for Pingré on his way to Rodrigué. This approach had some degree of success. On 25th November 1760, a general order was sent to the commanders of British vessels, with instructions 'not to molest his person or Effects upon any account, but to suffer him proceed without delay or interruption.'[9] Pingré was even furnished with a British passport.

Having taken 13 days to journey, together with half a ton of baggage, from Paris to the coast, Pingré departed from Lorient, in Brittany, on 9th January 1761. He later confessed to being terrified of the impending voyage—convinced he would never see his friends again. Notwithstanding the Admiralty's instructions, his voyage still involved cat-and-mouse games with the Royal Navy. His ship, the *Comte d'Argenson*, arrived at the Île de France on 6th May. From there he was taken to Rodrigué, where he landed on 28th May 1761, no doubt full of trepidation. 'We are informed,' he had been told by the Académie, 'that in the whole of this part of Africa the air, because of its bad weather in the rainy season, is very dangerous for foreigners.'[10]

The first task at Rodrigué was to ensure that all the instruments—clocks and telescopes—were in working order. A temporary observatory was set up—'I think there never was a more inconvenient one', grumbled Pingré, lamenting the fact that there were no masons or joiners on the island. His 'observatory' consisted simply of four large stones, placed in the open-air.

At this place, which 'had all the appearance of a skittle alley' [11], he took the elevations of stars with a quadrant, suspended his nine foot and eighteen foot telescopes from two poles and set up his pendulum clock. The clock was then calibrated against the timing of Jupiter's satellites. By the 6th June, the day of the transit, everything was ready. Everything, that is, except the weather! Rain, clouds and more clouds greeted Pingré and his assistant as they prepared to make the historic observations. How they must have cursed their wretched fortune! Part way into the transit, the skies cleared, but too late. They had missed the ingress of Venus. Consoling themselves with the thought that even measurements of the planet's positions on the Sun's disk and the corresponding times could be of some use, they applied themselves to this task. In the event, luck did not totally desert them, for, between gaps in the cloud, internal contact at egress was visible with perfect clarity. In common with many others, Pingré saw the disconcerting black-drop effect: 'At the exit of Venus…, the limbs [of the planet and the Sun], being not yet in contact, and even sensibly distant asunder,…I saw as it were a dark spot detach itself from Venus, and gain the limb of the Sun; at which instant I estimated the internal contact.' [12]

In the weeks following the transit, they set to, measuring the latitude and longitude of the observing station and surveying the island. Then calamity struck: on 29th June, a British man-of-war bombarded the island. Their ship was confiscated and the astronomers, together with the crew, were left stranded on the island.

Almost one hundred days passed before they were finally rescued. Even then, their tribulations were not at an end. On the way home they were attacked once again by a British ship. Eventually, Pingré landed at Lisbon and, abandoning the perils of the sea, made the rest of the way over land—arriving back in France, as he put it, 'one year, 3 months, 18 days, 19 hours, 53 and one half minutes after having left.' Clearly, he was glad to be back.

Although Jean-Baptiste Chappe d'Auteroche had initially intended to undertake the first leg of his journey to Siberia aboard a Dutch ship, delays in his preparations made him miss the ship. He decided to make his way overland instead and, as the vessel subsequently ran aground off the Swedish coast, he counted himself blessed with good luck.

Chappe left Paris at the end of November 1760. The war obliged him to take a route through some of the harshest terrain in Northern Europe. At times, temperatures were as low as 20 degrees below freezing. Icy

Jean-Baptiste Chappe d'Auteroche
(Woolf,Harry; The Transits of Venus, copy-right © 1959 by PUP. Reprinted by permission of Princeton University Press)

hills and frozen rivers had to be negotiated and accidents, with damaged equipment, were frequent. From Riga his party continued by sled to St.Petersburg. They left St.Petersburg on 10th March 1761 to cover the remaining 800 leagues to Tobolsk in Siberia by horse-drawn sleds. It was essential to make haste, before the thaw set in. If the snow melted, it would be impossible to get to Tobolsk in time. Only the sleds could manage the speed required and, without snow, they would be useless. The last river to be crossed had ice that was already covered by a layer of water. Six days after Chappe crossed it, the ice finally broke up.

He arrived in Tobolsk on 10th April. Immediately, he threw himself into preparations for the transit. The construction of an observatory on top of a nearby hill consumed so much of his attention that, at first, he was oblivious to the consternation that his presence in the locality had caused. The people of Tobolsk, driven by superstition and fear, were convinced that Chappe was a magician, bent on bringing evil into their midst. Catastrophic flooding, caused by snow-melt, subsequent to his arrival, reinforced this conviction:

'Some of the Russians advised me not to go alone to my observatory, and to take some precautions against the fury of the mob, which might lead them to any lengths. The advice was too prudent not to be followed, and from that time I determined to pass most nights in the observatory, lest they should attempt to pull it down.' [13]

Not discouraged by this undeserved hostility, Chappe continued his preparations. To calibrate his clocks and thereby find the longitude, Chappe could not use the moons of Jupiter, as Pingré had done: at such northerly latitudes, in summer, the sky was almost constantly lit by the Sun, thus obscuring the planets. Instead, he made observations of a solar eclipse: 'This eclipse being visible in Sweden, in Denmark and at St.Petersburg, I was sure of having observations corresponding to mine.' [14] By comparing his timing data with observations of the eclipse from Stockholm, supplied by Delisle, he was subsequently able to calculate the longitude of the Tobolsk observing station.

On the eve of the transit, Chappe recorded that, 'The sky was clear, the sun sunk below the horizon, free from all vapours; the mild glimmering of the twilight, and the perfect stillness of the universe, completed my satisfaction and added to the serenity of my mind.' [15] He slept that night in the observatory and awoke on the 6th June to be greeted by ideal weather.

When Chappe first saw Venus, it had already partly entered across the limb of the Sun. As he prepared to time the moment of internal contact, the importance of that fleeting moment seemed overwhelming. For this precise tick of the clock, he had travelled so far, and upon this single observation the hopes of astronomers throughout the world were so keenly focused. 'Although the sky was perfectly serene, yet my apprehensions were not yet at an end. The moment of observation was now at hand; I was seized with a universal shivering, and was obliged to collect all my thoughts in order not to miss it,' he recounted. At length, the black silhouette of Venus was to be seen at the critical point of *internal contact*: its disc fully visible, yet not separated from the limb of the Sun by even the slightest sliver of the Sun's own light. 'I felt an inward persuasion of the accuracy of my process', he wrote, 'Pleasures of the like nature may sometimes be experienced; but at this instant, I truly enjoyed that of my observation, and was delighted with the hopes of its being still useful to posterity, when I had quitted this life.' [16]

His hopes were not in vain. His observations were of the highest order of accuracy and continued to be used for more than one hundred years.

*****

In all, more than 120 astronomers, from at least eight nations, made careful observations of the 1761 transit of Venus, from about sixty stations. Mostly they were situated in the Northern Hemisphere, often at established observatories. Sweden in particular mounted an intense observing effort and, because of its northerly latitude, supplied results of great importance.

High expectations had preceded the transit. What conclusions could be drawn from the resulting plethora of observations and timings? Immediately, astronomers and mathematicians around the world started calculating. The resulting value for the solar parallax varied between 8.28" and 10.60". There was no consensus. Major factors in producing such a wide range of results were the black-drop effect and also the fact that the longitude of some of the farthest flung temporary observing stations was not adequately known. In the early 1760s, even the difference in longitude between the Greenwich and Paris observatories was only known to within 20"—about one quarter of a mile!

In one sense therefore, the results were disappointing, especially since Halley had predicted that 'by this means, the Sun's parallax may be discovered, to within its five hundredth part'. [17]

Nevertheless, the new values for the solar parallax, widely spread as they were, still represented a substantial advance on previous knowledge. Horrocks' speculative figure of 14" implied a distance of 60 million miles (95 million kilometres), but the 1761 figures, based on sound methods rather than speculation, implied a significantly greater distance of 77 million to 97 million miles (123 million to 157 million kilometres).

'I am afraid we must wait till the next transit, in 1769,' declared Maskelyne, 'which is, on many accounts, better circumstanced than this, before astronomers will be able to do justice to Dr.Halley's noble proposal, and to settle, with the last and greatest degree of exactness, that curious and nice element in astronomy, the sun's parallax, and thence determine the true distance of all the planets from the sun, and from each other.' [18]

CHAPTER 12

'HAPPY IS OUR CENTURY'

The shortcomings of the 1761 results did not dampen enthusiasm for observing the 1769 transit of Venus. In fact, the opposite occurred. Public interest grew and the expeditionary zeal devoted to the 3rd June 1769 transit was even greater than that for the previous one. This would be the last chance for one hundred and five years to extract from the motion of Venus, in its fullest precision, the reward promised by Halley.

In France, the industrious Joseph-Jerome de Lalande (1732–1807), a former pupil of Delisle, presented an updated mappemonde to the Académie des Sciences in March 1764, showing the differences in ingress and egress times for different places on the globe. This map provided both a catalyst and focus for the ensuing discussion of suitable places from which to observe the next transit.

Le Gentil, still in self-imposed exile at the other side of the world, decided that Manila, in the Philippines, would be an appropriate place for his observations. He wrote to colleagues in Paris, informing them of his intentions.

By the August of 1766, he was in Manila—'without contradiction one of the most beautiful countries in the seas of Asia.' He was ready to begin his preparations for the next transit. Pingré meanwhile had concluded, from the 1761 experience, that 'the method which was the simplest, the most natural, the easiest, the least susceptible to contradictions, of all those which could be used for deducing the solar parallax from a transit of Venus across the disk of the Sun, is the one which just uses the observed difference of durations in places where the parallax effect is most noticeably different'. [1] In other

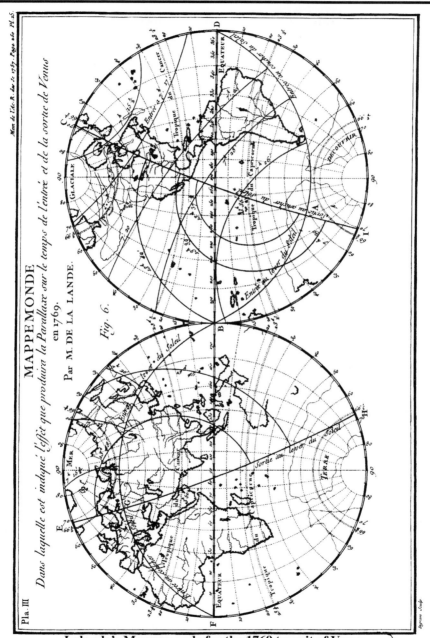

Lalande's Mappemonde for the 1769 transit of Venus
(Woolf,Harry; The Transits of Venus, copyright © 1959 by PUP.
Reprinted by permission of Princeton University Press)

words, the method proposed by Halley. It was known that the longest duration of transit would be observed from Lapland. Pingré pointed out that the ideal area for the shortest duration would be somewhere in the South Seas. Unfortunately, these waters were very poorly charted. Travellers, like Magellan, had often spoken of islands in the South Seas, but searching one out could prove difficult.

Le Gentil had been in Manila exactly eleven months when a letter from Lalande landed in his lap. In it, Lalande explained the latest thinking in

Paris about how the 1769 transit expeditions should be deployed. In particular, he outlined Pingré's latest thoughts. Le Gentil was taken aback: 'Monsieur de Lalande pointed out to me at the end of his letter that Monsieur Pingré had read at the Academy a memoir in which he complained that I was going too far; he would have wanted me to return to Pondichery.'[2]

Le Gentil graciously gave way to his older colleague. This time however, he was determined not to be late. He boarded a Portuguese vessel and landed at Pondichery on 27th March 1768: a full fourteen

Joseph-Jerome de Lalande
(Courtesy of the Observatoire de Paris)

months before the transit was due. He constructed a fine observatory on the site of the City's ruined fort and commenced gathering all the usual measurements, for determining time and position. This time, the war with England having ended, he didn't have to contend with hostile action from enemy ships. He had full co-operation from the English, even to the extent of being loaned a telescope by them.

Everything was set for a perfect observation. The weather in the months leading up to the transit was beautiful. What a contrast with his circumstances in 1761. Le Gentil was a truly happy man. 'The nights at Pondichery', he wrote, 'are of the greatest beauty in January and February; you cannot have any idea of the beautiful sky which these nights offer until you have seen them...During the whole month of May, until the third of June, the mornings were very beautiful...' [3]

At Pondichery the transit would take place during the early hours of 4th June and would already be in progress by the time the Sun rose. Le Gentil was too excited to sleep.

'Sunday the fourth, having awakened at two o'clock in the morning, I heard the sand-bar moaning in the south-east; which made me believe that the breeze was still from this direction...I regarded this as a good omen, because I knew that the wind from the south-east is the broom of the coast and that it always brings serenity; but curiosity having led me to get up a moment afterwards, I saw with the greatest astonishment that the sky was covered everywhere, especially in the north and north-east, where it was brightening; besides there was a profound calm. From that moment on I felt doomed, I threw myself on my bed, without being able to close my eyes.' [4]

As the day dawned, a violent storm broke out.

'The sea was white with foam, and the air darkened by the eddies of sand and of dust which the force of the wind kept raising continually. This terrible squall lasted until about six o'clock. The wind died down, but the clouds remained. At three or four minutes before seven o'clock, almost the moment when Venus was to go off the Sun, a light whiteness was seen in the sky which gave a suspicion of the position of the Sun, nothing could be distinguished in the telescope. Little by little the winds passed ... the clouds brightened, and the Sun was seen quite brilliant; we did not cease to see it at all the rest of the day...' [5]

Le Gentil was mortified.

'That is the fate which often attends astronomers. I had travelled about ten thousand leagues; I seemed to have traversed such a great expanse of seas, exiling myself from my motherland, only to be the spectator of a fatal cloud, which arrived in front of the Sun at the precise moment of my observation, snatching from me the fruit of my efforts and exertions...I was unable to recover from my astonishment, I had difficulty realising that the transit of Venus was finally over...At length I was more than two weeks in a singular dejection and almost did not have the courage to take up my pen to continue my journal; and several times it fell from my hands, when the moment came to report to France the fate of my operation...' [6]

It cannot have helped poor le Gentil to find out from friends that at Manila the transit had been visible in perfect blue skies!

To add insult to injury, when he returned to France, he discovered that, after eleven and a half years of absence, his relatives had given him up for dead and had divided up his estate.

Jean Chappe d'Auteroche meanwhile, had been sent to California—at that time entirely in Mexico. Like Le Gentil, he too was being dispatched to a location which was thousands of leagues from his first choice. His preferred location, the South Seas, had been blocked by political difficulties. For Chappe, however, the consequence of the redeployment would be considerably harsher than it had been for his luckless countryman.

His journey, by sea to Vera Cruz, overland through Mexico to San Blas, then by boat to the southern tip of the Baja Peninsula, took a full eight months. He was accompanied throughout by his engineer, Pauly, an artist, Noël, a watchmaker, Dubois, and the Spanish naval astronomers, Vicente de Doz and Salvador de Medina. They arrived on 19th May 1769, two weeks before the date of the transit. Chappe set up his observing station in a Spanish mission, at a village known today as San José del Cabo.

Upon arrival at the mission, he learned that the place was in the grip of a deadly epidemic disease—probably Typhus. One third of the population had already been carried off by it. With only days left to prepare for his observation of the transit, Chappe was fearful that a search for an alternative site would be too risky. Against advice, but confident of the sound constitution of the expedition members, he decided to stay at San José.

The observations of the 3rd June transit were impeccable. 'The weather favoured me to my utmost wish, I had full time to make accurate and repeated observations for the setting of my clock. At last came the third of June, and I had an opportunity of making the most complete observations.' [7] This was the last entry in his journal. Shortly after the transit, the village experienced a ghastly escalation of the epidemic.

'On the 5th of June, two days after they had observed the transit of Venus, Mr.Doz, Mr.Medina, and all the Spaniards belonging to them, to the number of eleven, sickened at once. This occasioned a general consternation; the groans of dying men, the terror of those who were seized with the distemper, and expected the common fate, all conspired to make the village of San José a scene of horror.' [8] Thus, Cassini de Thury, Director of the Paris Observatory, described the terrible events at San José.

Three-quarters of all the inhabitants died. Despite contracting the disease himself, Chappe continued his work. As the epidemic was raging about him, he got up from his sick bed on 18th June to make careful observations of a lunar eclipse, which helped to pinpoint his longitude and thus make the transit information complete. The exertion brought a worsening of his condition. Towards the end of July he said 'I know that I have only a little time left to live, but I have fulfilled my aim and I die content.' [9] On 1st August 1769, at the age of forty-one, he expired. Dubois, Doz, twelve soldiers, four Mexican officers and about fifty native American helpers also died. Only Pauly and Noël survived to bring back the sad story to France, along with the record of Chappe's observations.

The burial procession for Chappe d'Auteroche, San José del Cabo, 1769, as drawn by Alexandre-Jean Noël (*Courtesy of Réunion des Musées Nationaux*)

'His courage and endurance were unbounded,' declared Grandjean de Fouchy, a contemporary French eulogist of Chappe, 'what we have said of him affords more than one proof of that; only it would have been our heartfelt wish that the last proof of it which he gave, and which deserves so many commendations, had been less fatal to himself.' [10]

By comparison with his colleagues, Pingré, another veteran of the previous transit, had an almost routine visit to the island of Saint Domingo, in the West Indies, from where he successfully observed the transit using a 5-foot achromatic telescope. His observing companion, de Fleurieu, 'perceived a luminous little circle all round Venus, not yet entered more than about one third of her diameter. This luminous thread made, to all appearance, a perfect circle with the part of the circumference of Venus already advanced on the solar disk.' Pingré made a point of recording that, during their observations, 'everything was quiet and still, not a word was uttered, to intimate that anyone had observed the contact.' [11] Nine seconds was the spread of their independent timings of the first internal contact.

*****

The importance of setting up an observing station in Lapland, where the duration of the transit would be longest, was well recognised. In 1767, Christian VII, King of Denmark and Norway, invited a Jesuit priest, Father Maximilian Hell (1720–1792), to direct an expedition to Vardö, on the arctic coast of Lapland, for the purpose of observing the 1769 transit.

Father Hell had already established a solid reputation as director of the Vienna Observatory. Since 1757 he had edited the annual Vienna Astronomical Ephemerides—tables of daily-predicted positions for the Sun, Moon and planets. Because of his personal qualities, as well as his scientific acumen, Hell was held in high esteem by all who met him.

After obtaining the permission of his religious order and the imperial government of Austria-Hungary, Father Hell set off from Vienna on 28th April 1768, accompanied by Father Joannes Sajnovics and a botany student named Borgrewing. Travelling mainly overland, through Austria, Germany, Denmark and Norway, they arrived at Trondheim, from where they undertook the last leg of their journey by boat.

Upon arrival at Vardö on 11th October, they found conditions harsh and the snow 30 centimetres deep. Had Father Hell drawn the 'short straw' when observing stations were allocated? He probably didn't think so, for the Vardö site was arguably the most favourable one in the Northern Hemisphere. It was nearly on the meridian in which the middle of the transit would coincide

Father Maximilian Hell
(Courtesy of Prof.I.Bernard Cohen)

with midnight. But this was the 'Land of the Midnight Sun': the Sun would be still 3° above the northern horizon at this time. Provided that clouds did not intervene it would be possible to see the whole course of the transit during the night. Vardö , being on the night-time side of the Earth, would be moving in the same direction as Venus, due to the rotation of the Earth. The effect would be to make Venus appear to move more slowly and thus the transit would last longer. In the South Seas, by contrast, an observing station would be on the day-time side of the Earth and would move in the opposite direction to Venus, thus appearing to speed up the transit.

The day of the transit was very cloudy and yet Father Hell's party had the good fortune to see both the ingress and egress of Venus. The internal contacts occurred at 9.34pm and 3.33am respectively. Hell was jubilant. The success was celebrated by the firing of cannons and singing a rousing *Te Deum Laudamus*.

The results were promptly dispatched to Vienna and Copenhagen, by an armed courier. The party left Vardö on 27th June 1769, but their return journey was protracted. They did not arrive in Vienna until 12th August 1770, 27½ months after having left. In the meantime, Lalande, who was trying to collate all of the transit timings, wrote to Hell asking for a copy of the results. Hell refused to divulge the results ahead of publication in Vienna. Lalande became increasingly exasperated. He even hinted that the refusal of Hell could perhaps be because no results of value had been obtained. More mischievous people, perhaps motivated by anti-Jesuit prejudices, started rumours that Hell was waiting until he had seen other results, so that he could amend his own figures to agree—'cooking the books', so to speak.

In the event, all the insinuations melted away when 120 copies of Father Hell's report were printed in Denmark, even before he returned to Vienna. Also, his observations were presented to the Danish Academy of Sciences on 24th November 1769.

Little more was heard about the controversy, until, in 1835, Carl Ludwig Littrow (1811–1877), a successor of Father Hell at the Vienna Observatory, found the original diary which Hell had kept at Vardö. On examining the diary, he concluded that there was clear evidence of erasures and corrections, the times of the first interior contact of Venus having been re-written in a different colour of ink. Littrow's published report was thoroughly damning: truly 'scientific' evidence of Father Hell's guilt. Thus, forty-three years after his death, this unfortunate astronomer's reputation was completely destroyed.

Confidence in any calculations based on Hell's observations was severely undermined. George Airy (1801–1892), one of Flamsteed's successors at Greenwich, speaking in 1857, revealed the extent of the damage. 'In the transit of 1761, the result depended almost entirely upon an accurate knowledge of the differences in longitude of very distant stations, which are undoubtedly subject to great uncertainty. In the transit of 1769 it happened that the result depended almost entirely upon the observations made by Father

Hell at Wardhoe; and to these great suspicion has attached, many astronomers having, without hesitation, designated them as forgeries.' [12]

The story of Father Hell's 'dishonesty' looked set to become a sad foot-note in the annals of science. This, it would have become, had it not been for the curiosity, many years later, of the renowned American astronomer, Simon Newcomb (1835–1909).

In 1883, Newcomb was visiting the Vienna Observatory, attracted by the fine telescope, which had just been installed there by Grubb of Dublin. Due to the poor weather, he instead ended up spending most of his time in the library, researching for an intended re-assessment of the 1761 and 1769 transit observations. He asked for permission to see Hell's original diary, and, 'More as a matter of curiosity than with the expectation of reaching any definite conclusion,' [13] he compared the diary with Littrow's critique of it. He was astonished at what he saw. Littrow's description of the different ink colours was wholly inaccurate: all that seemed to have happened was that Hell had gone over the lettering again, with more ink, where the pen had run dry. Many of the alleged alterations were in fact made before the original ink had dried. The writer, on making a mistake, had simply rubbed it out with his finger. The alterations could not have been made at a later stage, when Hell had received the results of other observers.

Newcomb was puzzled. How could it be possible that Littrow had mis-taken the ink colours in the diary? This was the question he took to Weiss, Littrow's successor as Director of the Vienna Observatory. Was anything known as to the quality of Littrow's colour vision? 'Oh, yes,' came the prompt and decisive reply, 'Littrow was colour blind to red.' Even worse: 'He could not distinguish between the colour [red] of Aldebaran and that of the whitest star.' [14] No further investigation was needed. 'For half a century', said Newcomb, 'the astronomical world had based an impression on the inno-cent but mistaken evidence of a colour-blind man respecting the tints of ink in a manuscript.'

'The true state of the case seemed to me almost beyond doubt. It frequently happened that the ink did not run freely from the pen, so that the words had sometimes to be written over again. When Hell first wrote down the little figures on which, as he might well suppose, future generations would have to base a very important astronomical element, he saw that they were not written with a distinctness corresponding to their importance. so he wrote them over again with the hand, and in the spirit of a man who was determined to leave no doubt on the subject, little weening that the act would give rise to a doubt which would endure for a century.' [15]

The vindication of Hell was complete. His expedition to the arctic regions, the hardship suffered in the process and his honest record of the transit of Venus, could at last be judged in their proper light and found to be a truly valuable contribution to the progress of science.

*****

In Britain, the Royal Society figured prominently in the discussion of the 1769 transit. As early as 1763, the Society's *Philosophical Transactions* carried a diagrammatic summary of the event, prepared by James Ferguson. There was general recognition that every effort had to be bent to making use of this 'second chance'. Speaking to the Society in February 1765, the Oxford astronomer, Thomas Hornsby (1733–1810), delivered an impassioned appeal: 'An opportunity of observing another transit of Venus will not again offer itself until the year 1874. It behoves us therefore to profit as much as possible by the favourable situation of Venus in 1769, when we may be assured the several Powers of Europe will again contend which of them shall be most instrumental in contributing to the solution of this grand problem. Posterity must reflect with infinite regret upon their negligence or remissness, because the loss cannot be repaired by the united efforts of industry, genius or power.' [16]

The British preparations for the 1769 transit were based upon an analysis similar to that of Pingré. The method of durations was likely to offer the most promise of success. Attention likewise focused on the South Seas as *the* key location to aim for. This applied, according to Hornsby, 'whether it be proposed to determine the sun's parallax by the difference in the total duration of the transit, or by the observations of the internal contacts either at the ingress or egress.' [17] The Royal Society faced the same difficulty as the French, however, in procuring reliable maps of the area. Accounts of navigators over the previous three centuries were scoured for information about where land might be found in the Pacific Ocean.

In the November of 1767 the Society formed a Special Committee to discuss the preparations for the transit. The Committee's key members— Nevil Maskelyne, James Ferguson, James Short and John Bevis—each prepared a paper outlining the circumstances of the coming transit. Maskelyne, by now the Astronomer Royal, then formulated recommendations on the basis of these papers.

The Society resolved to send Joseph Dymond and William Wales to Hudson's Bay (Canada), William Bayly to North Cape (Norway) and Jeremiah Dixon to Hammerfest, off the Norwegian coast. But, it was the expedition to the South Seas, which was destined to capture the public imagination. The vessel to be used for this voyage had been built in 1764 at Whitby, Yorkshire, as the *Earl of Pembroke*. When the Admiralty purchased it in 1768, for £2,800, it was already looking decidedly worse for wear. Although less than four years old, it had been used as a coal bark, plying up and down the east coast of England. The spars were rotten. The rigging was a tattered remnant of former glory.

After a total refit, at Deptford Dockyard in August 1768, costing £2,294, the 368 ton vessel, under a new name, *His Majesty's Bark Endeavour,* was available for service in the South Seas. It was commanded by Lieutenant James Cook (1728–1779), a competent seaman with an unusual relish for the mathematical side of navigation. His observation of the August 5 1766 solar eclipse and calculation of the longitude in Newfoundland had already been reported to the Royal Society by John Bevis, who described Cook as 'a good mathematician and very expert in his business.' [18] He had no experience of commanding a ship or undertaking long voyages, but his quiet confidence persuaded his superiors that the Endeavour would be in safe hands. He was presented to the Council of the Royal Society on 5th May 1768 and at the same meeting Charles Green (1735–1771), a former assistant to Maskelyne at the Royal Greenwich Observatory, was nominated as astronomer to the expedition. Also sailing with Endeavour would be the respected botanist, Joseph Banks, accompanied by a group of naturalists and artists, personally financed by him. A truly scientific expedition.

Nevil Maskelyne had compiled a fresh set of instructions on how the transit was to be observed. He took special care to stipulate that each observer had to work completely independently in making timings. He didn't want a repeat of the mishap which had occurred at Greenwich during the 1761 transit. After that transit, when the results from the various observers around the world had been pooled, the results from Greenwich caused many a raised eyebrow. Three observers at the Royal Observatory had watched the planet's egress. At all other places where several observers had been stationed, each individual had judged the contact with the Sun's limb to occur at a slightly different time. The observation at Greenwich was an exception, as all three observers agreed to the second on the timing. Was this perhaps a case of fiddling the figures? Not quite. Thomas Hornsby, on a visit to Greenwich in 1762, found an embarrassingly human explanation. He was informed that, during the transit, Mr.Green, assisting with the observations, as soon as he

HM Bark Endeavour, a modern replica
(Courtesy of the HM Bark Endeavour Foundation. Photo - John Langley)

judged that the internal contact was formed, called out *'Now!'*. Thereupon, all the other observers instinctively stopped their stop-watches! In the dismissive words of James Short, who had furnished the telescopes for some of the expeditions, 'this observation can be looked on as no more than the observation of one person, and he too not much practised in observing.' [19]

Cook's original instructions simply required that he set up an observing station *somewhere* in the South Seas by June 1769. As luck would have it, just a few weeks before Cook was about to set sail, Captain Samuel Wallis returned from a voyage to the Pacific, announcing the discovery of Tahiti, or Ota-heite: an island 'such as dreams and enchantments are made of, real land though it was: an island of long beaches and lofty mountains, romantic in the pure ocean air, of noble trees and deep valleys, of bright falling waters.'[20] Cook's instructions were promptly revised. The Endeavour would sail for Tahiti, chauvinistically named *King George's Land* by its 'discoverers'.

In late August 1768, the Endeavour slipped out of Plymouth Harbour on the first of the voyages that would make Captain Cook a household name throughout Britain and beyond.

Once out of the English Channel, the Endeavour crossed the Bay of Biscay to the northern tip of Portugal, before striking out across the North Atlantic. After five weeks they arrived at the island of Madeira, where they took on provisions, including 3000 gallons of wine.

Cook's attention to the matter of fresh provisions, in particular fresh fruit, marked him out amongst his contemporaries. It also enabled him to conquer *scurvy,* the curse of long-distance seafarers. When Vasco da Gama sailed round the Cape of Good Hope in 1497, one hundred of his crew of 160 men died of scurvy. Anson, on his voyage around the world in 1740–4, lost 200 out of his 400 crew to the disease. The French navigator, Jacques Cartier (1491–1557), had graphically described the symptoms: 'Some lost their very substance and their legs became swollen and puffed up while the sinews contracted and turned coal-black and, in some cases, all blotched with drops of purplish blood. Then the disease would creep up to the hips, thighs and shoulders, arms and neck. And all the sick had their mouths so tainted and their gums so decayed that all the flesh peeled off down to the roots while the latter almost all fell out in turn.' [21] The usual outcome was sudden death, apparently from heart failure.

Cook recognised that scurvy was the result of prolonged consumption of a diet devoid of fresh vegetables and fruit. He made special efforts to ensure that his crews had regular supplies of fresh fruit. Onions, sauerkraut and beer made from spruce leaves were regular fare for the crew of his ship. All manner of exotic vegetables were introduced into the diet, whenever a supply was to be had. This was not always popular. It was no uncommon thing, according to one witness, for sailors to 'Curse him heartily and wish for god's Sake that he Might be Obledged to Eat such Damned Stuff

Captain James Cook
(© National Maritime Museum, London)

Mixed with his Broth as Long as he Lived. Yet for all that there were None so Ignorant as Not to know how Right a thing it was.' [22]

The Endeavour arrived at Tahiti on 13th April 1769 and dropped anchor in Matavai Bay. The welcome given by the Tahitians lived up to the expectations engendered by Wallis. Permission was given immediately for Cook's party to construct a fort and, within that, an observatory from which to view the transit. As the location for the observatory, the northernmost tip of the island was chosen. To this day, the place is called Point Venus.

As the day of the transit approached, Green and Cook anxiously watched the weather. Conditions on the eve of the transit did not augur well. The sky was cloudy. Nevertheless, on 3rd June Providence smiled on the astronomers. Cook recorded in his journal that, 'this day prov'd as favourable to our purpose as we could wish, not a Clowd was to be seen the whole day and the Air was perfectly clear, so that we had every advantage we could desire in Observing the whole of the passage of the Planet Venus over the Sun's disk.' [23]

Not everyone was involved, heart and soul, in the enterprise. Whilst most of the officers were ashore, watching the transit, some of the Endeavour's crew broke into its store-rooms and stole a large part of its stock of nails. The stolen nails were intended to form the currency for an illicit sexual trade with some of the Tahitian women, for whom, according to Cook, 'Nails, Shirts, &c were temptations that they could not withstand.' [24] Wallis's ship, the Dolphin, had almost been made unseaworthy by the crew pulling nails out of the timbers to engage in the same trade.

The observations were undoubtedly a success and much celebration took place that evening at Fort Venus. But, in the privacy of his diary, James Cook recorded a number of problems which seemed to place a strict limit on the accuracy which was achievable in timing transits of Venus. Not only did the infamous 'black drop' effect take place, but also an apparent penumbra around the planet and the tremors of the Earth's atmosphere, heated by the Sun's rays, added to the uncertainty. Cook, Green and another member of their group, Swedish botanist, Dr.Solander, had observed independently, as exhorted by Maskelyne, but their results were far from identical. 'We differ'd from one another in observeing the times of the Contacts much more than could be expected' [25], wrote Cook. He and Green differed by a full 20 seconds in their estimation of the exact moment of internal contact as Venus entered the Sun's disc.

'The first appearance of Venus on the Sun, was certainly only the penumbra, and the contact of the limbs did not happen till several seconds after, and then it appeared as in fig. the 4th; this appearance was observed both by Mr.Green and me; but the time it happened was not noted by either of us; it appeared to be very difficult to judge precisely of the times that the internal contacts of the body of Venus happened, by reason of the darkness of the penumbra at the Sun's limb, it being there nearly, if not quite, as dark as the planet. At this time a faint light, much weaker than the rest of the penumbra, appeared to converge towards the point of contact, but did not quite reach it, see fig. 2. This was seen by myself and the two other observers, and was of great assistance to us in judging of the time of the internal contacts of the dark body of Venus, with the Sun's limb. Fig. the 5th, is a representation of the appearance of Venus at the middle of the egress and ingress, for the very same phaenomenon was observed at both: at the total ingress, the thread of light made its appearance with an uncertainty of several seconds; I judged that the penumbra was in contact with the Sun's limb 10" sooner than the time set down above; in like manner at the egress the thread of light was not broke

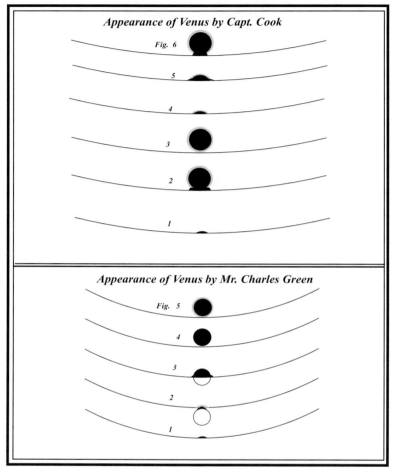

off or diminished at once, but gradually, with the same uncertainty: the time noted was when the thread of light was wholly broke by the penumbra. At the total egress I found it difficult to distinguish Venus's limb from the penumbra; which of course made the second external contact a little doubtful, and the precise time that the penumbra left the Sun could not be observed to any degree of certainty, at least by me. Some of the other gentlemen, who were sent to observe at different places, saw at the ingress and egress the same phaenomenon as we did; though much less distinct, which no doubt was owing to their telescopes being of a less magnifying power; for the penumbra was visible through my telescope during the whole Transit; and Dr.Solander, whose telescope magnified more than ours, saw it, I have reason to think, distincter than either Mr.Green or myself; though we both of us saw enough to convince our senses, that such a phaenomenon did indisputably exist, and we had a good opportunity to observe it, for every wished-for favourable circumstance attended the whole of that day, without one single impediment, excepting the heat, which was intolerable: the thermometer which hung by the clock and was exposed to the sun as we were, was one time as high as 119°' [26]

It was more than a month before the Endeavour departed from Tahiti. The voyage of exploration was to last a further two years before the crew, or, at least, some of them, would see their homes again. Ahead of them lay the survey of New Zealand and the charting of the east coast of Australia. In that time, almost half of the crew perished from dysentery and malaria, contracted in Batavia. Charles Green was amongst those who perished, thus increasing to three the number of astronomers who had died in the 1769 transit expeditions. The Captain's journal recorded that, 'in the night Died Mr. Charls Green who was sent out by the Royal Society to Observe the Transit of Venus; he had long been in a bad state of hilth, which he took no care to repair but on the contrary lived in such a manner as greatly promoted the disorders he had had long upon him, this brought on the Flux which put a period to his life.' [27] He was buried at sea.

In order to help fund Cook's expedition, the Royal Society had petitioned King George III (1738–1820) for funds of £4,000. The King had responded enthusiastically. His imagination was well and truly caught by the purpose of the venture. He commanded that an observatory be built at Richmond (now Kew), so that he too could observe the transit. The observatory was designed by Sir William Chambers, with no expense spared: a magnificent building of Portland stone, surmounted by a moveable dome. It was ready by the time of the transit and was placed under the superintendence of Stephen Demainbray, a one-time itinerant lecturer on popular science. It had been Demainbray's lectures many years earlier which had kindled a keen interest in science in the youthful king.

On the day of the transit, the King was accompanied at the telescope by Queen Charlotte and a number of other notables. Demainbray was charged with taking a note of the time, as the King observed. Strangely, although the observatory, as can be imagined, was equipped with the best instruments for

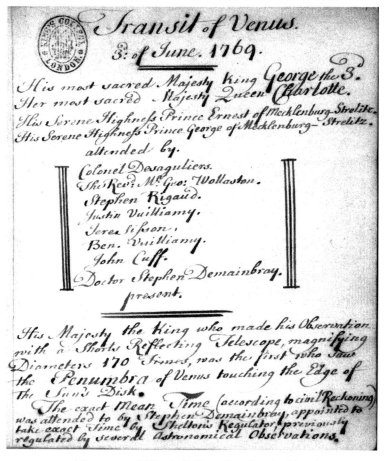

(Courtesy of King's College London Archives)

the purpose, the results were never published. Whether the King had considered, like the young Tycho, that publishing was beneath the dignity of his station, or whether his reticence to go into print was for fear of submitting his efforts to scrutiny by others, we can only speculate.

The international effort put into the 1769 transit greatly exceeded the unprecedented energy devoted to that of 1761. The telescopes and other instruments had significantly improved and the position of Venus on the Sun was more propitious to Halley's method of durations. Sadly, a definitive value for the solar parallax still eluded astronomers. More than 600 separate papers on its value were delivered to the world's scientific bodies.

As the results were sifted however and more refined analysis of the observations was completed, inadequate or suspect data being filtered out, it became clear that the mean solar parallax had been confined to a much narrower range: between 8.43 seconds and 8.80 seconds, comparing favourably with the modern value of 8.794148 seconds. The corresponding range for the distance of the Sun was 90 million to 94 million miles.

Typical of the more discriminating analyses was that presented to the Royal Society in December 1771 by Thomas Hornsby, Savilian Professor of Astronomy at Oxford University. Hornsby used the observations from just five locations: Vardö, in Lapland (Father Maximilian Hell); the Kola Peninsula, between the Arctic Ocean and the White Sea (Stepan Rumovsky); Hudson's Bay (Joseph Dymond and William Wales); California (Jean Chappe d'Auteroche); and Tahiti (James Cook and Charles Green).

On this basis he derived a solar parallax, at the time of transit, of 8.65". He then concluded: 'The parallax on the 3rd of June being 8.65", the mean parallax will be found to be = 8.78"; and if the semi-diameter of the Earth be supposed = 3985 English miles, the mean distance of the Earth from the Sun will be 93,726,900 English miles. And, as the relative distances of the planets are well known, their absolute distances, and consequently the dimensions of the solar system, will be as follows.' [28]

	Relative distance	Absolute distance (miles)
Mercury	387.10	36,281,700
Venus	723.33	67,795,500
Earth	1,000.00	93,726,900
Mars	1523.69	142,818,000
Jupiter	5,200.98	487,472,000
Saturn	9,540.07	894,162,000

At last it could be said that the true distance of the Sun had been discovered. Not only that, but, on the basis of Kepler's Third Law, the distance to every other planet could now be computed.

Amongst scientists everywhere there was a strong sense that a milestone in human knowledge had been reached. Summing up the mood, the famous French astronomer, Cassini de Thury, observed: 'Happy is our Century, to which has been reserved the glory of being witness to an event which will render it memorable in the annals of the Sciences!' [29]

With more restrained language, but scarcely less satisfaction, Hornsby, addressing the Royal Society, declared that, 'from the observations made in distant parts by the astronomers of different nations, and especially from those made under the patronage and direction of this Society, the learned of the present time may congratulate themselves on obtaining as accurate a determination of the Sun's distance, as perhaps the nature of the subject will admit.' [30]

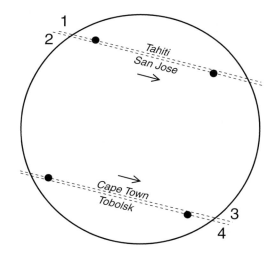

**The path of Venus across the Sun in 1761 and 1769
from different observing sites, to scale
1761: Cape Town (3) and Tobolsk (4)
1769: Tahiti (1) and San José del Cabo (2)**

CHAPTER 13

VENUS ABANDONED

The results gathered by astronomers, often at great personal cost, during the 1761 and 1769 transits of Venus, continued to be re-assessed for more than a hundred years afterwards. Unfortunately, each time the matter was subjected to fresh analysis, a new figure for the Sun's distance came to the fore. Sometimes the figure drifted up, sometimes down—like a shifting sand-dune, under the action of each fresh tide.

In 1825, Johann Franz Encke (1791–1865), then director of the Seeberg observatory near Gotha in Germany, published a comprehensive discussion of the available material. In it, he arrived at the quite low value of 8.577″ for the solar parallax. The implied distance of the Sun was 95 million miles. His conclusion was regarded as authoritative and it entered into the popular domain. Generations of school children were taught this distance and committed it to memory as one of the certainties of modern science. A flavour of the respect for Encke's re-assessment was given in Robert Grant's *History of Physical Astronomy*, published in 1852: 'When we consider the ingenuity of the method employed in arriving at this determination, and the refined nature of the process by which it is carried into effect, we cannot refrain from acknowledging it to be one of the noblest triumphs which the human mind has ever achieved in the study of physical science.' [1]

Grant's assurance was reminiscent of the earlier confidence of Thomas Hornsby in a smaller figure for the distance. In the case of Grant and his contemporaries, it turned out to be the *pride before a fall*. It was not long before Encke's figure was thrown into question by results obtained from other techniques. Peter Hansen (1795–1864), of Gotha, got 8.916″ for the solar parallax from examination of the Sun's influence upon the Moon; the French physicist Léon Foucault obtained 8.86" from using a technique related to the velocity of light; Stone and Winnecke gave 8.943" and 8.964", based on observations of Mars. As more and more relatively large values cropped up, there grew a tendency amongst astronomers to reject Encke's value and, with it, the usefulness of transits of Venus.

Even so, the romance associated with the transit of Venus and the sheer weight of astronomical endeavour invested in the method still continued to exert a pull. Mary Somerville (1780–1872), who continued with scientific work into her nineties, lamented that not living 'to see the distance of the Earth from the Sun determined by the transit of Venus', [2] would be one of her chief regrets in dying.

The final salvo for the transit of Venus method was in 1891. The brilliant US Navy astronomer, Simon Newcomb, subjected the eighteenth century transit observations to a thorough and sophisticated re-analysis. 'We should not consign to oblivion a mass of material so celebrated in the history of science', [3] he explained, by way of apology for use of material which others might have regarded as outdated. Previous analyses were taken to task for being too selective. The trouble stemmed from Halley's prediction that a very high degree of timing accuracy could be achieved. Astronomers had taken this to heart. Consequently, 'the exaggerated opinion of the accuracy with which transits of inferior planets over the Sun could be observed has resulted, in accordance with a law of human judgement, in impairing the value of the conclusions derived from observations of these phenomena. It was assumed that the observations were not legitimately liable to a probable error of more than a few seconds, and a temptation was thus offered to treat them on this hypothesis. This led to a

Simon Newcomb *(Courtesy of the US Naval Observatory Library)*

habit of too freely rejecting discordant observations, and produced an undue bias in favor of such as could be brought into good agreement with others. It having been found that the results obtained in this way were erroneous to an extent which was not supposed possible, and therefore that the supposed precision of the observations was illusory, there now exists a tendency to look upon them as too inaccurate for further discussion.' [4]

With over 200 observations to pick from, previous analysts had tended to use only those which seemed to give the best agreement with the currently favoured range for the solar parallax. The objective, scientific method had been forgotten and subjective influences were subtly taking over. No doubt about it, thought Newcomb. 'A comprehensive view of the order of progress in determining the constants of astronomy will show', he argued, 'a decided bias in each generation of astronomers towards depending upon a few recent observations supposed to be accurate, to the exclusion of past ones supposed to be affected by undiscoverable sources of error.' [5] In contrast, rather than consigning large numbers of observations to the scrap heap, he assigned confidence weightings to them. These he derived from a completely fresh reading of all the first hand reports of the observers. The resulting new value for the solar parallax was 8.79", agreeing very well with the modern value.

Governments had given liberal grants to send expeditions to observe the 1874 and 1882 transits of Venus. Above all, astronomers had desired to test the utility of a powerful new tool: photography. Nevertheless, it was clear, even by the middle of the nineteenth century, that observing transits of Venus across the face of the Sun might never produce the desired accuracy for calculations of the Sun's distance.

The drawbacks were well-established: the unsteadiness of the telescopic images, caused by hot air currents in the Earth's atmosphere, and the infamous *black drop* effect distortion of Venus' shape when in contact with the Sun's limb. The use of photography during the 1874 transit did not improve matters. In fact, it turned out to be a big let-down. The edge of the Sun was too poorly defined on the resulting photographic plates to allow accurate measurement to take place. The report rendered to the Royal Astronomical Society by Captain G.L.Tupman, head of the British expeditions, made woeful reading: 'When the [photographic] negatives are placed under the microscope with an amplification of only 5 or 6 diameters, the limbs of both

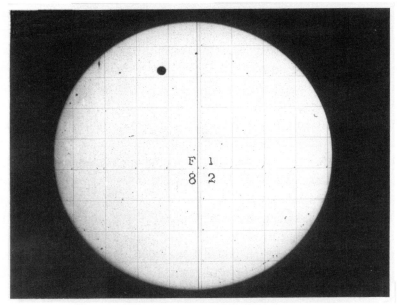

**A US Naval Observatory expedition photograph of
one of the nineteenth century transits of Venus**
(Courtesy of US Naval Observatory)

planet and Sun, even those which are pretty sharp to the unaided eye, become extremely indistinct, and the act of bisecting the limb with the wire or cross of the micrometer is mere guesswork. The deposit of silver fades off gradually to nothing, and the denser the film the broader is the zone of fading off, and the more uncertain the measures.'[6] Such was the disappointment, that some institutions which had sent expeditions did not even bother to publish the results.

Many investigators had already turned their backs on Venus and were looking to other methods. In particular, measurements of the parallax of the planet Mars offered an attractive alternative.

Mars is nearest to the Earth when it is in *opposition*. That is, when Mars and the Earth are roughly in line with the Sun—Mars being on the dark side of the Earth. These oppositions occur every fifteen or seventeen years. At roughly 0.37 astronomical units (1 astronomical unit = the mean Earth-Sun distance), the nearest approach of Mars is not as close as that of Venus (0.27AU). Even so, it might still be possible to measure the parallax effect with sufficient accuracy. The image of the planet would be much steadier than that of Venus in transit: observations would be at night and there would be no 'boiling' effect caused by the heat of the Sun.

In essence, the method was simple. As Mars crosses the local meridian, round about midnight, its position, relative to the stars, is noted by staff at two different observatories. If the observatories are widely separated in latitude, then the position noted at one observatory will be slightly different from that at the other. This angular displacement of the planet is due to a combination of the motion of Mars, in the interval between the two observations, and the parallax effect. The rate at which Mars moves is known. Therefore, if the displacement is also known, together with the distance between the observatories, then it is possible to calculate the distance of Mars by fairly straightforward triangulation. Armed with Kepler's Laws, the distance of Mars could be used to calculate the distance of the Sun, and hence the *solar parallax*.

Thus, in 1862, using measurements of the position of Mars made at Greenwich in England and the Cape in South Africa, E.J.Stone calculated the solar parallax.

The great convenience of Mars was shown even more strikingly in 1877 by David Gill (1843–1914), later Her Majesty's Astronomer at the Cape. Gill had come late to astronomy. The beautiful clock on his mantelpiece, fashioned with his own hands, bore witness to another life. Only seven years previously he had been locked into a wholly different career. He was in charge of a prosperous family clock business in Aberdeen. Before that, he had studied sciences at the University of Aberdeen. There, under the tutelage of the

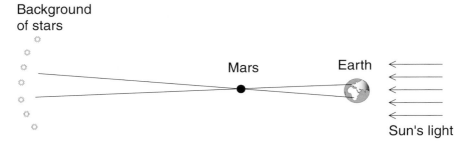

The parallax of Mars. The planet appears displaced against the background stars when viewed from different locations

celebrated physicist, James Clerk Maxwell, he acquired a deep desire to embark on a life of scientific investigation. It appeared however that this was not to be. His father, fifty-four years his senior, was anxious that he should take over the family business and, out of deference to his father's wishes, he reluctantly agreed. For ten years David Gill ran the clock business, characteristically mastering every detail of it. Then, one day in 1863, he made a visit to Edinburgh that awakened a passion for astronomy, which

David Gill

was to change his life. The visit was to the Calton Hill Observatory—at that time under the supervision ofCharles Piazzi Smyth. Professor David Thomson, of Aberdeen, had supplied him with a letter of introduction to Piazzi Smyth: 'I have been requested by Mr.David Gill Jr whose father is a watchmaker in this place and who is desirous of introducing here the time-gun system, which owes its origin to yourself, to give him a few lines of introduction and to secure for him the advantages of your aid and advice in carrying his intentions into effect.' [7]

'This was my first introduction to an astronomer and an observatory,' noted Gill. 'I was received with every possible kindness, and shown every detail not only of the time-gun and time-ball arrangements, but of all the instruments at the observatory.' [8] He was bowled over by all that he saw of the time-service. This was just his cup of tea and he was sure that a similar service would be of great use to Aberdeen. Although, truth to tell, it would soon be superseded, as Greenwich time invaded the entire land, through the agency of the railway network, Piazzi Smyth's time-service was responsible for bringing Gill into the irresistible embrace of astronomy. From that moment onward, he became increasingly absorbed by the astronomical measurement of time.

As his love of astronomy grew, he became more and more disenchanted with his choice of career. He had a secure, comfortable life in Aberdeen. An ideal position, perhaps, from which a dilettante could pursue a passion for astronomy, but Gill was not of this mould. After marrying Isobel Black, he decided, in 1872, with her full agreement, to take the plunge. He resolved to dispose of his interests in the family firm and start working as a professional astronomer. He was offered a post as private astronomer to Lord Lindsay (later the Earl of Crawford), an enthusiastic amateur, who was busy establishing a new observatory at Dun Echt, about thirteen miles from Aberdeen. 'To accept Lord Crawford's kind and generous offer was a heavy pecuniary loss,' he admitted, 'but a gain so great in the prospective interest of my life that I had no hesitation in accepting it gratefully.' [9]

Things moved quickly. By 1874, Gill was in Mauritius, with Lord Lindsay, observing the transit of Venus. He brought to the task a new way of determining the longitude of the observing station: telegraphy. Greenwich time was relayed by way of telegraph lines. A complicated chain of telegraph links was established: Greenwich—Berlin—Malta—Alexandria—Suez—Aden. The last link—Aden to Mauritius—was completed by transporting chronometers. Fifty of them, to be precise! It was not surprising, given his clock-making background, that Gill devoted such efforts to getting the right time to Mauritius. Even so, he was well aware of the limitations of transits of Venus for calculating the solar parallax. He set his sights on other methods.

In 1877, the opposition of Mars occurred within a few days of Mars being at its nearest to the Sun. As a result, its approach to the Earth was the closest for more than thirty years. Astronomical institutions the world over, eager to take advantage of this circumstance, cooperated in observing from widely separated sites. The US Naval Observatory issued a circular letter, urging a combined effort, on a suitable pre-arranged plan. Compared with the expensive transit of Venus expeditions, the opposition of Mars was a gift. It would 'afford a favorable opportunity for…the determination of the solar parallax with little or no extra expense to those governments or individuals already provided with meridian circles in fixed observatories,' [10] said the letter. Many such observatories duly prepared.

Gill himself, funded by the Royal Astronomical Society and the Royal Society, embarked on an expedition to Ascension Island, with the express purpose of observing the event. He took with him a heliometer, loaned by Lord Lindsay. It consisted essentially of a telescope whose object glass was divided into two semi-circular pieces, capable of sliding by each other. Each half of the lens made its own independent image of the objects—say two neighbouring stars—which were being examined. Properly setting the half-lenses, by means of a screw adjustment, the two images could be made to coincide. The displacement of the lenses was measured, by means of a microscope, on a finely divided scale. The reading then permitted the angular distance between the stars to be calculated with a precision unattainable by any other process known at the time.

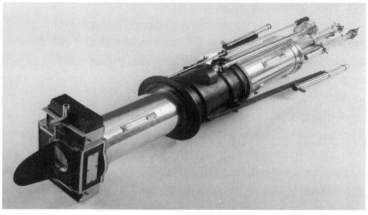

Lord Lindsay's Heliometer
(Courtesy of the Royal Observatory, Edinburgh)

With the heliometer, Gill intended to measure the position of Mars amongst the stars when seen in the east, in the evening, and then in the west, in the early hours of the morning. Thus, from a single site, which had moved its position, due to the Earth's rotation and orbit, the parallax effect could perhaps be gauged. Of course, given the time which would elapse between observations with this approach, it would be necessary to take account of the angular distance moved by Mars in its own orbit.

With the exception of the much larger heliometer in the Radcliffe Observatory at Oxford, Lindsay's instrument was the only one in the country.

Naturally enough, it aroused a great deal of interest and preparations were made to exhibit it to members of the Royal Astronomical Society, prior to its departure for the South Atlantic. The catastrophe which ensued, proved to be, at once, almost the undoing of the expedition, but also, paradoxically, its salvation. The instrument was erected in the Burlington House meeting rooms of the Society in London. All that remained to be done was to adjust the inclination of the polar axis of the heliometer to the angle appropriate for the latitude of Ascension Island, 8°S. The instrument had never been used at such a southerly location before and, to everyone's surprise, the adjusting screw proved to be too short for the southern hemisphere!

Isobel Gill described the scene: 'David was applying a level to an inclined piece of wood cut to the angle of the latitude of Ascension, and was directing the workmen to give final motion to the screw by which the inclination of axis is changed, when slip! the screw gave out, the overhanging weight of the Heliometer and its counterpoises tore the lower end of the cradle from his hand, and, tilting upwards, the polar axis, counterpoise weights and Heliometer tube, in all several hundredweight, came down crash, from a height of 7 or 8 feet, upon the floor.

'Imagine the astronomer's feelings as he saw the Heliometer of all his hopes light upon its delicate eye-end; that eye-end driven through the floor and slowly torn off, as the whole mass gradually turned round, smashing and crushing the more delicate rods, handles and other attachments…

'As the whole thing lay there on the floor, within ten days of the time when it must be packed for shipment, it seemed impossible that it could be restored fit for use.' [11]

Fortunately, upon examination, it was found that all the vital parts of the heliometer—its object glass, slide and scales—were still intact. Within six days, the services of the foremost instrument makers in the land having been enlisted, the heliometer was repaired. 'Had it not been for this trial in Burlington House,' observed Isobel, 'in all probability, a like accident would have happened at Ascension, the result of which would simply have meant the utter failure of the expedition.' [12]

By mid-July 1877, the Gills, together with 20 tons of baggage, were on Ascension Island: an inhospitable land, consisting largely of cinders and lava flows, deriving from its volcanic origin.

Later, in her fascinating journal, *Six Months in Ascension: An Unscientific Account of a Scientific Expedition*, Isobel described their immediate feelings: '…That first evening after sunset…we could speak of nothing, think of nothing, but the beauty of the heavens. Though Ascension was barren, desolate, formless, flowerless, yet with such a sky she could never be unlovely. The stars shone forth boldly, each like a living fire. Mars was yet behind Cross Hill, but Jupiter literally blazed in the intense blue sky now guiltless of cloud from horizon to zenith; and, thrown across in graceful splendour, the Milky Way seemed like a great streaming veil woven of golden threads and sparkling with gems. The Southern Cross—a poem in the heavens— shone out a bright welcome to us…" [13]

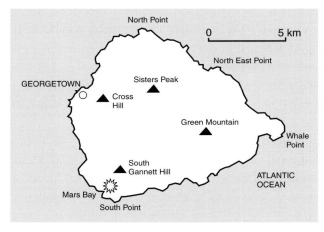

Ascension Island

An observatory was immediately set up at Garrison (Georgetown), the only inhabited part of the island, but as the time of opposition approached, it became clear that this choice of place, in the lee of the 890 metre high Green Mountain, was far from ideal. The initial good weather gave way to persistent cloud, which eventually became a serious threat to the entire venture. 'Fearful of losing one hour of starlight we watched alternately for moments of break in the cloud, sometimes with partial success, but more frequently with no result but utter disappointment, and the mental and physical strain, increasing every night, grew almost beyond our strength.' [14]

Gill faced a dilemma. At this late stage he dared not leave the observatory to search for a more suitable site, and yet, without a new site, there was a risk that all would be lost. Isobel volunteered to go off in search of a more suitable site. Eventually, she found one, much freer from cloud, but it was at the other side of the island: South Point. A new dilemma thrust itself upon Gill. There were no roads to the proposed site. The only way to get there was by a time-consuming trek over rocky country or by landing from a choppy sea. Either way, there were risks. 'On the one hand my husband felt,' recounted Isobel Gill, 'If I stay here and fail, I shall have failed also in my duty, not having done my utmost. On the other hand, every night is now of importance, and a week lost certainly, if I pull down the Observatory, while the slightest accident to an instrument here, with no one to repair it, will be fatal to the expedition. Yes! both "ifs" were unpleasant, but the first was intolerable, and after a day of anxious thought David made up his mind that an attempt to reach South Point must be made.' [15]

A party of eight helpers carried the precious heliometer across treacherous terrain—part of the way, to the consternation of Gill, on their heads!

Within five days of setting up at the new location, subsequently known as Mars Bay, successful morning and evening observations were made, much to Gill's relief. In all, satisfactory observations were secured on 32 evenings and 25 mornings. The angular distance of Mars was measured from 22 different comparison stars. The resulting value for the solar parallax was 8.78", with a probable error stated to be no greater than 0.012" either way The implied distance of the Sun was between 92,981,000 and 93,235,600 miles.

The idea of using observations of Mars in this way was not original to Gill. The first Astronomer Royal, John Flamsteed, had done something similar more than two hundred years earlier. On 10th November 1672, he wrote to Oldenburg, the Editor of the Royal Society's *Philosophical Transactions*: 'Last September I was at Towneley the first week that I intended to have observed Mars. There with Mr. Towneley I twice observed him [Mars], but could not make two observations as I intended in one night. The first night after that of my return I had the good hap to measure his distances twice from two stars the same night: whereby I find that his parallax was very small certainly not 30 seconds: so that I believe the Sun's is not more than 10 seconds.' [16]

Flamsteed was so amazingly close, that one might wonder whether it was really necessary for all those eighteenth century transit of Venus expeditions. In fact, however, the closeness of his figure of 10 seconds is deceptive. The crudeness of his instruments gave no guarantees that 10 seconds was anything other than an indicative figure: a well-educated guess. Edmond Halley must have been aware of Flamsteed's letter, and yet, half a century later, was assuming that the solar parallax would be about 12½ seconds—not 10. 'To confess the truth,' wrote Halley in 1716, 'it is hardly possible for a man to distinguish, with any degree of certainty, seconds, or even ten seconds, with instruments, let them be ever so skillfully made.' [17]

There is no doubt that measurement of such a tiny quantity as the parallax of Mars does demand a fine telescope, equipped with an accurate micrometer. How strange therefore to find that the great Tycho Brahe, observing with the naked eye, and using a method similar to that of Flamsteed, claimed to have found a discernible parallax. In truth, such a feat would have been impossible. The parallax of Mars—that is, the difference in direction of Mars for observers who are separated by one Earth-radius—can amount to 23 arc seconds *at most*. This is equivalent to the breadth of a hair on the back of your hand, at the end of an outstretched arm! No wonder that Kepler, trying to repeat Tycho's measurements, during the Martian opposition of 1604, concluded that the whole idea was decidedly ill founded. 'I would be insane to rely on these observations for anything so subtle', [18] he confessed. He probably suspected himself of being insane for even trying: it was a freezing February night—so cold that his bare hands stuck to the sextant—and the bitter wind prohibited the use of lamps. The sextant's scales could only be read by the light of a glowing coal.

In 1857, George Airy, one of Flamsteed's successors at Greenwich, resurrected the idea of using this method - expressing a view that, for measuring the Sun's distance, 'this method is the best of all.' [19] Confident that observing instruments had improved dramatically since the era of Flamsteed and Halley, he felt sure that results of some value might now be obtained. Gill's success with the heliometer provided ample confirmation that this was true.

CHAPTER 14

VENUS RECLAIMED

Science sometimes progresses by means of gradual improvements of known methods, but every now and then a new discovery will be made which allows a qualitative leap forward.

During the evening of 14th August 1898, a thirty-one year old German astronomer, Gustav Witt (1866–1946), made just such a discovery which

Gustav Witt *(Courtesy of Archenhold-Sternwarte Berlin-Treptow)*

enabled the Sun's distance to be determined with an unparalleled degree of precision.

An astronomical career had almost eluded Witt. Modest family circumstances had obliged him to pay his way as a student by holding down a job as a stenographer at the Reichstag. Ironically, the demands of this job prevented him from successfully completing his studies. The only route into professional astronomy was to become an employee of the newly founded Urania people's observatory in Invalidenstrasse, Berlin.

On that fateful evening, accompanied by an observatory assistant, Felix Linke, he had been making long exposure photographs of the night sky, with the aim of finding known minor planets—or asteroids—which had not been observed for some time. He hoped in this way to obtain measurements which would lead to a better determination of their orbits. The telescope upon which the camera was mounted was tracking the movement of the stars. Consequently, stars would appear as pinpoints of light on the photographic plates, but any body moving relative to the stars would hopefully be 'smeared' across the plate—showing up as a line.

Many years later, Linke described what happened: 'For the purpose of finding Planetoid Eunike (No.185) which had not been seen for years, we centred the plate on the star *beta* Aquarius during the night from August 13 to August 14, 1898, and I exposed the plate for two hours. Eunike had to be in that area....Next morning, after the plate had dried, the plate was checked and it was found that both Eunike and another known planetoid had been registered. But a third and longer line drew our attention. It was so long (0.4 millimetres) that we first thought it to be a flaw in the emulsion, but it was too clean to be that, hence we suspected an actual object with a high rate of apparent motion, a comet. Since the evening of August 14 was again clear, we could look for the suspicious object with the 12-inch refractor of the Urania Observatory, at that time the largest telescope anywhere in Prussia. A few quick measurements proved that it had such an unusually fast movement as had never been observed for a minor planet. Its appearance spoke against the thought that it might be a comet; it was a tiny dot of light without any appendages...' [1]

The faint object that had been sighted was indeed a minor planet, or asteroid, initially known as Planet DQ, and later named *Eros*.

Swarms of asteroids exist in orbit around the Sun, mainly concentrated in the wide gap between the orbits of Mars and Jupiter. The first to be discovered was found by the Sicilian astronomer Piazzi in 1801. He named it *Ceres,* after the Goddess of Agriculture and patron Goddess of Sicily. Pallas, Juna, Vesta and many more were to follow.

Eros was the 433rd asteroid to be discovered: a lump of rock, no more than 15 miles in diameter. It was far too faint to be visible to the naked eye—in many ways a totally insignificant body. In one vital respect however, it was to prove extremely important: a succession of observations showed that it was locked into a highly elliptical orbit which would bring it, every 37 years, much closer to the Earth than either Mars or Venus.

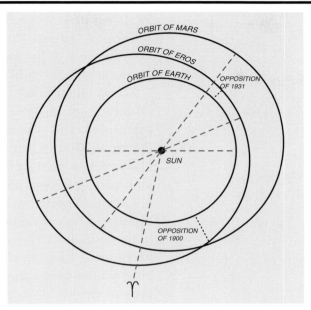

The orbits of Earth, Mars and Eros, showing the 1900 and 1931 oppositions of Eros *(based on a US Naval Observatory Library plate)*

Unfortunately, Witt discovered it shortly after one of its closest approaches in 1894, but computation quickly showed that in 1900–01 it would pass within 30 million miles of the Earth and in 1930–31 it would be even closer— only 16.2 million miles away.

The usefulness of these orbital features was immediately grasped. 'The next opposition, 1900 November and December', explained Simon Newcomb, 'will be unusually favorable for measurements of the parallax...In January, 1931 an opposition very near perihelion is likely.

'Owing to the unusual character of the orbit of DQ, its geocentric motion will sometimes present singular features. At perihelion its linear velocity in its orbit is very near that of the earth. Hence, should an opposition occur, the geocentric longitude will be nearly stationary for several days.'

He urged colleagues around the world, at the next opposition, to fix its position among the stars from hour to hour by the photographic telescope and the heliometer. 'The combination of observations in the Eastern and

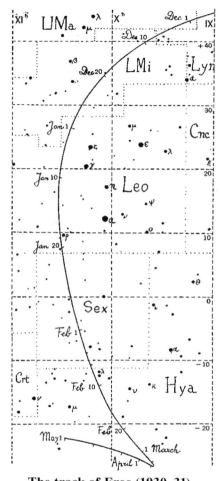

The track of Eros (1930–31)
(from Popular Astronomy, 1930)
**In mid-January it had a movement
of up to 1 degree per day in latitude,
but was virtually stationary in
geocentric longitude, as predicted
by Newcomb**

Western hemispheres will then, it may
be hoped, suffice for the best
determination of the solar parallax
yet made by direct measurement.' [2]

Masses of measurements were
taken at both of these favourable
approaches. This was especially so
during 1930-31, when twenty-five
observatories throughout the world
took part in a joint, photographic,
observing campaign with their best
equipment. By careful measurement
of the positions of Eros amongst the
background stars, on almost 3,000
photographs taken from different
parts of the world, its parallax and
distance could be determined. As with
Mars, the application of Kepler's
Laws could then give the distance of
the Sun.

Beside being nearer than Mars, and
thus having a greater parallax, Eros,
being very tiny, had the advantage of
being visible only as a point of light,
rather than as a disc. Its apparent
position was therefore easier to pin-
point.

The analysis of the data took the
best part of ten years. The result was
not published until 1942, by which
time many of the participating
countries were on opposing sides in
a World War: a war which robbed an aging Witt of house, books and
manuscripts and also destroyed the Urania observatory within which he had
made his invaluable discovery. It was probably some time before all

contributing astronomers got to know the outcome of their joint labours. The precision of the result, printed on paper conforming with the 'authorized war economy standard', exceeded expectations. The new value for the mean solar parallax, 8.790", calculated by Harold Spencer Jones (1900–60), the British Astronomer Royal, was stated to be accurate to within a thousandth part of one second. The implied mean distance of the Sun was 93,005,000 miles (149,675,000 km), with an uncertainty either way not exceeding 9000 miles (17,000 km).

Spencer Jones was keen to emphasize the remarkable degree of accuracy which had been achieved. 'The uncertainty in the newest determination of the Sun's parallax', he wrote, 'corresponds to the apparent breadth of a human hair at 10 miles!' A great achievement, indeed. In fact, he declared it to be 'the goal for which

Harold Spencer Jones
(Courtesy of the Royal Astronomical Society)

astronomers have so long been striving…the final word has been said on the historic problem for many years to come and the fundamental distance in astronomy has been measured with all the accuracy that is needed.' [3]

Maybe the accuracy *was* sufficient for any practical needs, but 'the final word'? Not so. At the very time when Spencer Jones and his assistants were painstakingly labouring over the 1931 Eros observations, the invention of RADAR (Radio Direction and Range finding) was creating a tool that could provide an improved method of determining the solar parallax. By a curious twist of fate, the new method brought the planet Venus back centre-stage in the quest for the solar parallax.

On the 10th and 12th February 1958, the Millstone Hill radar installation of the Massachusetts Institute of Technology Lincoln Laboratory was directed towards Venus. About two weeks earlier the planet had just made its closest approach to the Earth, some 28 million miles distant.Twelve years previously radar signals had been bounced off the Moon successfully, but Venus was more than a hundred times further away. The echo, if one could be discerned, would be considerably fainter. Detection equipment would need to be 10 million times more sensitive.

The 26 metre diameter steerable dish at Millstone Hill was a product of the Cold War. Spurred on by the Soviet Union's detonation of its first nuclear bomb, in September 1949, the US military had provided almost ninety percent of the funding for the Lincoln Laboratory. The early work of the Laboratory was directed at developing radar systems which could warn against aeroplane attack. Within a short space of time though, it became clear that the most

The 26 metre radar antenna at Millstone Hill *(Reprinted with permission of MIT Lincoln Laboratory, Lexington, Massachusetts)*

deadly threat might be from Inter-Continental Ballistic Missiles (ICBMs). These missiles could carry nuclear warheads high above the ionosphere. Conventional radar systems were useless for their detection. Not only did the missiles represent extremely tiny targets, hundreds of kilometres above ground level, but also they could be mimicked by meteors and various disturbances of the ionosphere.

The Millstone Hill radar installation was part of an experimental ICBM warning system. It began operation in October 1957 and amongst its first tasks was the study of potential sources of false alarms, including the Moon, auroras and meteors. Venus, the object of its attention in the February of 1958, was rather a sideline—a proving ground for the technical prowess of Millstone Hill. MIT staff members Bob Price and Paul Green decided that the installation was just about up to the job of getting an echo from the planet.

Five attempts, or 'runs', were made and, of these, the results of four were processed. The procedure adopted was to transmit skyward, in the direction of Venus, pulses of a 440 MegaHertz radio signal. Each pulse lasted for 2 thousandths of a second and a gap of 33 thousandths of a second was left between each pulse. After sending this train of pulses for 4½ minutes, the transmitter was switched off and the installation was put into listening mode. In two of the attempts there was no evidence whatsoever of a return signal over and above the background radio noise. In the other two, however, about five nail-biting minutes after the start of transmission, small peaks in the received signals, seemed to indicate that unbelievably faint echoes had been received. 'When we saw the peaks, we felt very blessed', recalled Price. Yet, so faint were the 'echoes', that, even after a detailed statistical analysis of the received signals, some element of doubt lingered on. 'We looked into our souls about whether we dared go public with the news', [4] Green admitted.

The precise round trip travel time of the signals was put at 295.5065 seconds for 10th February and 302.9842 seconds for 12th February. Radio signals travel at the speed of light. Assuming that this was 299,860 kilometres per second, the Lincoln Laboratory staff calculated the distance that the returned signals must have traveled. From the known distance of Venus on the days in question, in astronomical units, the distance to the sun and therefore the solar parallax could be calculated. The solar parallax was put at 8.8022". Opinion from an independent consultant proved favourable and

20 March 1959, Volume 129, Number 3351

SCIENCE

Radar Echoes from Venus

Advances in several arts made possible this experiment
in radio astronomy performed during the IGY.

R. Price, P. E. Green, Jr., T. J. Goblick, Jr., R. H. Kingston,
L. G. Kraft, Jr., G. H. Pettengill, R. Silver, W. B. Smith

The possibility of obtaining radar echoes from celestial bodies outside the Earth-Moon neighborhood, and the scientific value of information obtainable from such echoes, has been discussed by Kerr (1) and others (2). The attainment of such objectives has been brought from the realm of theoretical interest to within the range of experimental accomplishment with the advent of (i) receiving amplifiers having low noise, such as the maser, (ii) high-power missile-tracking radar transmitters employing steerable antennas of large aperture, and (iii) flexible and stable digital data-processing techniques.

On 10 and 12 Feb. 1958, about 2 weeks after Venus' closest approach, signals from M.I.T. Lincoln Laboratory's Millstone Hill radar installation (2a) were directed toward Venus. That planet was then about 28 million statute miles from the Earth, and the time required for radar signals to reach Venus and return was about 5 minutes. The equipment was operated with the characteristics shown in Table 1. With these specifications, it should be possible to detect the planet near its time of closest approach to the Earth, provided that the planet is a good reflector at 440 megacycles per second and that the reflection is reasonably coherent over the pulse length. Under such conditions, a signal-to-noise

The authors are members of the staff of Lincoln Laboratory, Massachusetts Institute of Technology, Lexington.

ratio of – 10 decibels should be obtained at the output of a filter matched to a single received pulse when Venus is at a distance of 28 million miles. By repeated pulsing of the transmitter and proper integration of the received signal over several thousand pulses, a signal-to-noise ratio can be built up that is sufficient to establish the presence of the return unequivocally.

Data Collection and Processing

Five separate runs were made, and data from four of these have been processed. In each run signals were transmitted for approximately 4.5 minutes; the transmitter was then turned off, and the receiver output was recorded on magnetic tape for the following 5 minutes.

Because of the uncertainty in the size of the solar system, which is several times the normal interpulse period employed (33.3 milliseconds), it was decided to code the transmission in such a way that range ambiguities could be resolved. For this purpose, the normal stream of transmitted pulses occurring 33.3 milliseconds apart was gated on and off by a binary maximal-length shift-register sequence (3). The transmitted waveform then had the appearance of a periodic train of 2-millisecond pulses, except that half of them were deleted in a pseudo-random fashion.

The transmitter used a high-power

klystron, and the stability of the entire transmitter-receiver conversion chain held to within 1 cycle per second during the 10-minute period of each run. A three-level, solid-state maser (4) with a potassium (chromi) cobalticyanide crystal in a bath of liquid helium was employed with a directional coupler to provide the low-noise receiving front end.

In receiving, a spectral zone 3 kilocycles per second wide, centered roughly 20 kilocycles below the transmitted carrier in order to pass the Doppler-shifted radar return, was accurately converted down to an intermediate frequency lying in the audio region. After the amplitude of this signal was quantized into 64 levels by means of an analog-to-digital converter operating at a sampling rate of 12 kilocycles per second (crystal-controlled), the signal was recorded on magnetic tape for later processing by an IBM Type 704 electronic digital computer.

In processing, the recorded data are first passed through the digital equivalent of a matched filter whose impulse response is a sinusoidal pulse 2 milliseconds long. The frequency of the sinusoid is deduced from the expected Doppler due to Earth-Venus motion and Earth rotation, together with the known receiver conversion frequencies. The envelope of the filter output is then squared and cross-correlated against a replica of the transmitted envelope; proper compensation is made for the Doppler shift in the pulse repetition frequency caused by the receding motion of the planet. Cross-correlations were taken at 1-millisecond increments in the relative delay between the reference and the squared filter output, until a region of uncertainty of approximately 600 milliseconds had been completely explored.

Results

Of the four runs that have been processed, two show no evidence of radar returns. Each of the other two, however, exhibits in its cross-correlation function statistically significant evidence of a return, as is shown in Fig. 1. Figure 1 shows that portion of each of the final

Price and Green went ahead with publication. The result appeared in the journal *Science*, 13 months after the pioneering observations.

President Eisenhower sent a telegram giving his congratulations on 'a notable achievement in our peaceful ventures into outer space.'[5] Price and

Green were immediately treated to national television and newspaper coverage. If they had wanted to quietly await the verdict of their peers in the scientific community, they were out of luck.This high profile turned out to be unfortunate, as when the next inferior conjunction of Venus arrived in September 1959, everything started to unravel. Although Manchester University's newly operational radio telescope at Jodrell Bank, Cheshire, reported a successful duplication of the American results, Millstone Hill itself failed to detect any echo at all. This was especially puzzling, since the Millstone Hill transmitter power was now almost twice the 1958 level. Green was mystified. With another colleague, Gordon Pettengill, he commented: 'It is difficult to explain the disparity between the results obtained at the two Venus conjunctions. Our current feeling is that the planet's reflectivity may be highly variable with time, and that the two successes in 1958 were observations made on very favorable occasions.' [6] An internal report of NASA's Jet Propulsion Laboratory (JPL), circulating in 1961, put forward a more sceptical interpretation: 'It is not known at the present time with certainty that a radio signal has ever been reflected from the surface of Venus and successfully detected.' [7] Eventually, the 1958 results were repudiated, even by their originators. Pettengill, writing in a 1968 Lincoln Laboratory publication, observed that 'the apparently successful runs, on February 10 and 12, indicated unambiguous values for echo delay which were self-consistent to within 0.002 sec. out of some 300 sec ... Because these two observations were remarkably self-consistent in range, it seemed quite unlikely that both indications could have been caused by noise alone. Despite this evidence, later incontrovertible observations yield a value for the astronomical unit which differs by almost 1 part in 1000 from the one obtained from this experiment. No satisfactory explanation for the results of this early experiment has ever been found.' [8]

Near the desolate Goldstone Dry Lake, in the Mojave Desert, California, JPL had its own large dish antennas. With these, JPL researchers hoped to be the first to detect an unmistakeable echo from Venus. Walt Victor and Bob Stevens, the managers of the project, reckoned that the equipment at Goldstone, primarily intended for spacecraft communications, constituted 'the most sensitive operational receiving system in the world.' [9]

On 10th March 1961, a month before inferior conjunction, the Goldstone dishes were pointed at Venus. For two full months the experiment continued. Over 238 hours of recorded radar data was collected. This time there was no ambiguity about the echoes. Victor and Stevens calculated a new value for the Astronomical Unit: 149,599,000 kilometres, with a probable maximum error, either way, of 1,500 km. The new value was more than 100,000 km

One of the two 26 metre antennae at Goldstone, used by JPL to detect echoes from Venus in 1961 *(Courtesy of NASA/JPL/Caltech)*

larger than the 1958 result from Millstone Hill. Convincing support for the new value came from similar experiments carried out in 1961 by the pioneering team at Millstone Hill and at Jodrell Bank and Yevpatoriya in the Crimea (USSR). Results from all four sites gave values for the Astronomical Unit which were spectacularly close to each other. All were within a three thousand kilometre range. There was now no doubting the effectiveness of the radar method. It was as if human beings had reached out, with unbelievably frail fingers, and lightly touched Venus itself: the reincarnation of Aristotle's long-forgotten 'visual ray'.

After this success, following conjunctions were used to repeat the procedure and refine the results. The technology was in the throes of very rapid development. Dish sizes and transmitted power were increasing by leaps and bounds. Within a decade, Irwin Shapiro in the *Scientific American* journal could report that the Lincoln Laboratory's Haystack radar facility in Tyngsboro, Massachusetts, was able to receive echoes of 10^{-21} Watt power: 'far less power than would be expended by a housefly crawling up a wall at the rate of one millionth of a meter per year.' [10]

By 1964, results from radar had converged so much that identical figures were routinely being given by the different radar establishments. In that year, on the basis of the radar results, the General Assembly of the International Astronomical Union agreed to adopt 149,600,000 km as the Astronomical Unit and 8.794" as the solar parallax.

On 4th October 1957 the world had moved into a new era: the 'space-age'. As the rocket carrying Sputnik 1 hurtled up through the atmosphere above the Soviet Union, a field of human endeavour opened up in which the exact value of the Astronomical Unit—the Earth-Sun distance—ceased to be a matter of simply theoretical interest. The accuracy with which it was

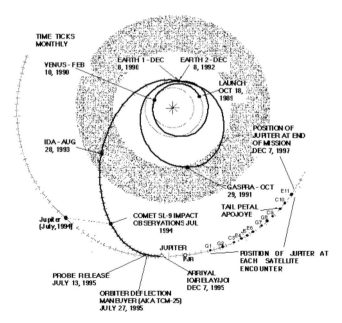

The Galileo Venus-Earth-Venus gravity assist trajectory to Jupiter
(courtesy of NASA)

177

known began to have an extremely practical bearing. In order to calculate trajectories for space-craft, the distances and orbital elements of the Moon and the planets needed to be known with the utmost precision.

The complicated journeys of discovery undertaken during the closing years of the twentieth century are testimony to how well the Sun's distance is now comprehended. The six year voyage of the NASA probe, Galileo, after its launch in 1989, would otherwise have been inconceivable. The sheer artistry of its interplanetary ballet—calling at Venus, two asteroids and twice at the Earth, en route to Jupiter—was absolutely dependent upon this comprehension. The value for the solar parallax currently accepted is that adopted in 1976 by the International Astronomical Union—8.794148"—and the corresponding mean distance of the Sun is 92,958,329 miles (149,597,870 kilometres).

Isaac Newton, acknowledging his debt to his predecessors, once remarked to Robert Hooke, 'If I have seen further than other men, it is because I have stood on the shoulders of giants.'[11] As we marvel at the achievements of our own generation in dispatching sophisticated instruments, with unerring accuracy, to the farthest reaches of the Solar System, we too stand indebted to a succession of 'giants' whose strivings and sacrifices led to the discovery of that most elusive of physical quantities—the true distance to the Sun.

CHAPTER 15

THE COMING TRANSITS OF 2004 AND 2012

On the eve of the 1882 transit of Venus, William Harkness (1837–1903) of the US Naval Observatory mused: 'There will be no other till the twenty-first century of our era has dawned upon the earth, and the June flowers are blooming in 2004. When the last transit occurred the intellectual world was awakening from the slumber of ages, and that wondrous scientific activity which has led to our present advanced knowledge was just beginning. What will be the state of science when the next transit season arrives God only knows. Not even our children's children will live to take part in the astronomy of that day.' [1]

We can identify with Harkness, organiser of the US 1882 expeditions, in feeling a sense of awe when contemplating the changes which might occur in more than one hundred years of human history. Maybe this is but a fleeting moment in the cosmic scale of things. On the human level

William Harkness (*Courtesy of the US Naval Observatory Library*)

however, it is time enough for generations to have lived out their lives. When the dramatic sight of Venus on the face of the Sun is next seen, not one soul will be living who was witness to the last such conjunction.

In our own epoch, we are blessed with not one, but two, opportunities to see this strange spectacle. On 8th June 2004 and 5th–6th June 2012 transits of Venus will occur. Not until the year 2117 will another opportunity arise.

Only two people are known to have seen the 1639 transit of Venus. A few hundred, at most, saw the 1761 and 1769 transits. Tens of thousands probably saw those in 1874 and 1882. The transits of 2004 and 2012 will occur in a period when television has spread its satellite suspended tentacles across the globe. It is likely that hundreds of millions will be able to watch the entire progress of the transits from the comfort of their own homes—wherever they live. Possibly these will be the most viewed astronomical events in history

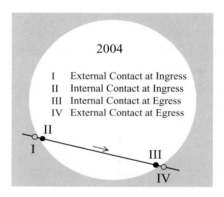

The track of Venus across the Sun, 8th June 2004

Large parts of the world's population will be able to see the whole of the 2004 transit, from beginning to end with their own eyes. Most of Europe, the Asian sub-continent, the Middle East and Eastern Africa will be ideally placed. China, Japan, Australasia, Western Africa, the eastern areas of North and South America will only see part of the transit.

As seen from the very centre of the Earth's sphere, the 8th June 2004 transit will commence at approximately 5-13am Greenwich Mean Time and will finish at 11-26am. For observers on the Earth's surface, of course, the same parallax effect which our forebears exploited to determine the Sun's distance, will cause slightly different times, depending on the observer's location.

The 2012 transit will begin at around 10-09pm GMT on 5th June and will finish at 4-49am on 6th June. North America and the Pacific areas should see the ingress and Australasia, Asia, Eastern Africa, the Middle East and Eastern Europe should see the egress.

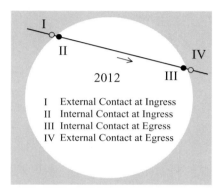

The track of Venus across the Sun, 5th-6th June 2012

The transits will be visible to the naked eye, but on no account should they be viewed with unprotected eyes. To try viewing in this way could lead to instant and permanent blindness. Sunglasses, smoked glass, exposed film and other non-specialist aids are dangerously inadequate for eye-protection and should be avoided. The Sun can be safely viewed, for short periods, through protective Mylar film or certain grades of welders' visors, but the safest method of viewing is to project the Sun's image onto a piece of white paper through binoculars or a small telescope, as did Horrocks in 1639. Never look directly at the Sun with the naked eye!

Perhaps you will have the good fortune to see the transit of 2004 or 2012, without the interposition of clouds. Maybe you will only catch a brief glimpse, due to clouds, or simply due to where you live. Hopefully, the story related in these pages will be brought to mind. It is a tale of insatiable human curiosity and of the incredible spirit of inquiry, which launched our ancestors upon intrepid voyages across the globe to witness a tiny spot upon the face of the Sun: a spot which offered the promise of revealing the dimensions of the Solar System.

It might be thought that a transit of Venus is a purely telescopic wonder, or a matter of interest simply to astronomers. Let us therefore conclude with

LOCAL CIRCUMSTANCES OF THE 2004 TRANSIT OF VENUS

Location	INGRESS								EGRESS								Duration between Internal Contacts		
	External Contact				Internal Contact				External Contact				Internal Contact						
	Day	h	m	s	Day	h	m	s	Day	h	m	s	Day	h	m	s	h	m	s
Berlin	June 8	5	19	38	June 8	5	39	25	June 8	11	3	23	June 8	11	22	51	5	23	57
Buenos Aires	June 8	5	14	31	June 8	5	34	16	June 8	11	13	32	June 8	11	32	46	5	39	16
Cairo	June 8	5	19	39	June 8	5	39	4	June 8	11	4	32	June 8	11	23	39	5	25	27
Cape Town	June 8	5	16	56	June 8	5	36	0	June 8	11	11	9	June 8	11	29	51	5	35	8
Lima	June 8	5	14	9	June 8	5	34	14	June 8	11	11	43	June 8	11	31	20	5	37	29
London	June 8	5	19	49	June 8	5	39	43	June 8	11	4	1	June 8	11	23	31	5	24	17
Madrid	June 8	5	20	18	June 8	5	40	11	June 8	11	5	25	June 8	11	24	49	5	25	13
Montreal	June 8	5	16	52	June 8	5	37	12	June 8	11	5	14	June 8	11	25	14	5	28	2
Moscow	June 8	5	18	45	June 8	5	38	23	June 8	11	2	1	June 8	11	21	30	5	23	38
New Delhi	June 8	5	16	4	June 8	5	35	8	June 8	11	1	30	June 8	11	20	42	5	26	22
New York	June 8	5	16	46	June 8	5	37	7	June 8	11	5	51	June 8	11	25	49	5	28	43
Paris	June 8	5	19	57	June 8	5	39	49	June 8	11	4	12	June 8	11	23	41	5	24	23
Rome	June 8	5	20	7	June 8	5	39	50	June 8	11	4	29	June 8	11	23	49	5	24	39
San Francisco	June 8	5	12	23	June 8	5	32	35	June 8	11	3	42	June 8	11	23	57	5	31	7
Shanghai	June 8	5	12	6	June 8	5	31	12	June 8	10	59	33	June 8	11	19	8	5	28	21
Sydney	June 8	5	7	17	June 8	5	26	5	June 8	11	5	53	June 8	11	25	15	5	39	48
Tehran	June 8	5	18	23	June 8	5	37	41	June 8	11	2	40	June 8	11	21	52	5	24	59
Tokyo	June 8	5	11	9	June 8	5	30	23	June 8	10	59	15	June 8	11	19	2	5	28	51
Wellington (NZ)	June 8	5	6	46	June 8	5	25	44	June 8	11	7	34	June 8	11	27	1	5	41	49

Not visible (Sun below the local horizon). No allowance has been made for atmospheric refraction.

This table has been compiled using the algorithms and orbital elements presented in Transits by Jean Meeus (Willmann-Bell, 1989). All times are given as Universal Time (same as GMT). Corrections need to be made for the local Time Zone.

LOCAL CIRCUMSTANCES OF THE 2012 TRANSIT OF VENUS

Location	INGRESS								EGRESS								Duration between Internal Contacts		
	External Contact				Internal Contact				External Contact				Internal Contact						
	Day	h	m	s	Day	h	m	s	Day	h	m	s	Day	h	m	s	h	m	s
Berlin	June 5	22	4	4	June 5	22	21	53	June 6	4	37	13	June 6	4	54	50	6	15	20
Beunos Aires	June 5	22	8	30	June 5	22	26	35	June 6	4	31	52	June 6	4	50	15	6	5	16
Cairo	June 5	22	5	46	June 5	22	23	44	June 6	4	37	51	June 6	4	55	25	6	14	7
Cape Town	June 5	22	9	54	June 5	22	28	11	June 6	4	35	24	June 6	4	53	23	6	7	13
Lima	June 5	22	6	55	June 5	22	24	49	June 6	4	31	3	June 6	4	49	26	6	6	14
London	June 5	22	3	36	June 5	22	21	23	June 6	4	37	12	June 6	4	54	52	6	15	49
Madrid	June 5	22	3	32	June 5	22	21	23	June 6	4	37	41	June 6	4	55	25	6	16	18
Montreal	June 5	22	3	34	June 5	22	21	13	June 6	4	33	29	June 6	4	51	28	6	12	16
Moscow	June 5	22	5	5	June 5	22	22	53	June 6	4	36	38	June 6	4	54	10	6	13	45
New Delhi	June 5	22	9	8	June 5	22	27	5	June 6	4	34	57	June 6	4	52	25	6	7	52
New York	June 5	22	3	38	June 5	22	21	18	June 6	4	33	21	June 6	4	51	22	6	12	4
Paris	June 5	22	3	41	June 5	22	21	29	June 6	4	37	23	June 6	4	55	3	6	15	54
Rome	June 5	22	4	12	June 5	22	22	4	June 6	4	37	47	June 6	4	55	26	6	15	43
San Francisco	June 5	22	6	21	June 5	22	23	56	June 6	4	29	21	June 6	4	47	22	6	5	25
Shanghai	June 5	22	10	57	June 5	22	28	46	June 6	4	30	59	June 6	4	48	30	6	2	13
Sydney	June 5	22	15	56	June 5	22	34	0	June 6	4	26	9	June 6	4	44	9	5	52	8
Tehran	June 5	22	6	49	June 5	22	24	45	June 6	4	36	49	June 6	4	54	19	6	12	5
Tokyo	June 5	22	10	41	June 5	22	28	25	June 6	4	29	47	June 6	4	47	22	6	1	22
Wellington (NZ)	June 5	22	15	30	June 5	22	33	34	June 6	4	25	16	June 6	4	43	26	5	51	42

Not visible (Sun below the local horizon). No allowance has been made for atmospheric refraction.

This table has been compiled using the algorithms and orbital elements presented in Transits by Jean Meeus (Willmann-Bell, 1989). All times are given as Universal Time (same as GMT). Corrections need to be made for the local Time Zone.

a report printed in the *Honolulu Commercial Advertiser* on 12th December 1874, following the observations in the Hawaiian Islands by the British Transit Expedition of 1874.

'The long-awaited celestial phenomenon has been most satisfactorily observed at this point; and the success of the eminent astronomers now residing here is a cause for rejoicing in this community. During the day there was a very general demand for broken panes of glass and bottles, which were smoked and held in readiness for looking at the sun at 3:30 o'clock, when the great celestial event was predicted to take place. The natives were as busy with their preparations for astronomical observations as the white foreigners. Little Kanakas were going about the streets with pieces of blackened glass in hand, for the purpose of looking, as they said, at the Hokulaa, the Morning Star, go through the sun, which they expect will be hereafter burnished with an increased solar splendor.

'It was curious to listen to the remarks and speculations of natives whose savage fathers had never suspected this occasional spot on the great light of day. They knew that Lono, or Captain Cook, the discoverer of these isles, had come to these seas to observe a star in the sun, and it had been predicted in his day that it should be seen again more than a hundred years afterward on this day, with the hour and the minute, and the very second specified. And now there were ten thousands throughout these isles looking upward to prove the truth of this century-old prediction.

'At a few minutes past 3, you could see everywhere in the streets faces looking upward to the sun, with a piece of shaded glass in hand to screen his fierce rays from man's weak, yet ambitious, searching eyes. A minute or two elapsed, and no change in the dusky red ball above. Another minute gazing upward, and still no spot flecks the face of the sombre rubescent orb. Ha!— "aia la!"—there it is, cries one keen-sighted, close watching Kanaka; and now we begin to see, a little to the right of the top or vortex of the sun, a slight dent or notch; and as we gaze on, the dent or spot enlarges, advances within the borders of the disc; and as the clearly-defined dark macula upon the ruddy plane is now distinctly seen by every eye, an enthusiastic native says, "Surely they who beheld this were prophets, and Lono was a prophet..."'[2]

TRANSIT OF VENUS - 8 JUNE 2004
View of the Earth from Venus

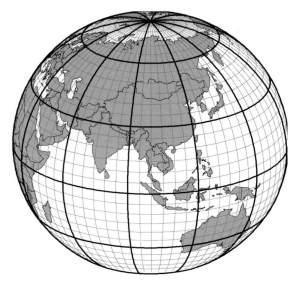

5h 13m UT: External Contact at Ingress

11h 26m UT: External Contact at Egress

Mapbase © ESRI, 1999

TRANSIT OF VENUS - 5–6 JUNE 2012
View of the Earth from Venus

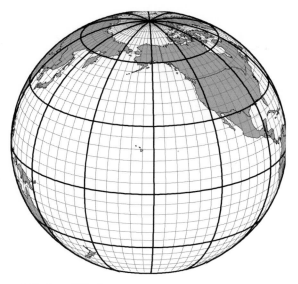

22h 9m UT: External Contact at Ingress

4h 49m UT: External Contact at Egress

Mapbase © ESRI, 1999

ACKNOWLEDGEMENTS

This book could never have been completed without access to the excellent collections and helpful staff of the Science Museum Library (London), the Royal Astronomical Society Library, Liverpool Central Library, and Manchester Central Library. Special thanks are due to the staff of the Edward Boyle Library of the University of Leeds. A great deal of the content of the book emanates directly from the basement stacks and other resources of that impressive institution.

My thanks go to the following individuals: June Marsden, Frances Bernstein and John Clare for valuable comments on various versions of the manuscript; William Dumpleton, for a thorough guided tour around the historic Dunsink Observatory, which features in the prologue to the book, in the summer of 1999; Alex Pratt, for translation of material from Astronomische Nachrichten; and, Andrew Murray, for helpful advice on some eighteenth century sources.

Whilst researching and preparing the book, I have received regular, unsolicited emails from many individuals around the world, who have contacted me in relation to my web-site on this topic. I have made use of many of their comments and suggestions. Above all, I have received much encouragement from the enthusiasm they have shown for the subject. For good or for ill, they have unwittingly helped to sustain my commitment to this project, whenever it might have been about to flag.

Finally, I would like to thank my partner, Jane, for critical comments on countless versions of the manuscript and for acting as an ever-patient 'sounding board', along with my sons, Andrew and Graham, over the several years it has been in preparation.

NOTES

Chapter 1 PROLOGUE: DUBLIN, 1882

1   Ball,R.S., *The Story of the Heavens*, Cassell, 1886, p.185
2   Ball,W.V., *Reminiscences and Letters of Sir Robert Ball*, p.110
3   Ball,R.S., *Op.Cit.,* p.187
4   Ball,R.S., *Op.Cit.,* p.187
5   Ball,R.S., *Op.Cit.,* p.188

Chapter 2 WANDERING STARS

1   Ball, W.V., *Reminiscences and Letters of Sir Robert Ball*, p.196
2   Plutarch, *On the Face in the Moon*, 16, p.292B
3   Heath, Sir T.L., *Aristarchus of Samos*, p.78
4   Heath, Sir T.L., *Greek Astronomy*, p.27
5   Aristotle, *On the Heavens*, II, chapter XI, 291b (Loeb edition, 1939, p.201)
6   Aristarchus, *On the Sizes and Distances of the Sun and the Moon*, reproduced in Heath, Sir T.L., *Aristarchus of Samos*, p.353
7   *Ibid.*, p.353
8   *Ibid.*, p.353
9   Plato, *Phaedo*, 109A-110A (Loeb edition, 1914, p.375)

Chapter 3 HEAVENLY SPHERES

3   Lucretius, *On the Nature of Things*, tr. Smith, M.F., 1969, p.185
2   Sagan, C. and Druyan, A., *Comet*, p.24
3   Heath, Sir T.L., *Greek Astronomy*, p.80
4   *Ibid.*, pp.76-77
5   Sambursky, S., *Physical Thought from the Pre-Socratics to the Quantum Physicists: An Anthology*, 1974, p.111
6   Ptolemy, C., *Almagest*, Book 1, Chapter 7, tr Toomer, G.J.,1998, p.45
7   Heath, Sir T.L., *Op.Cit.*, p.lvii
8   Copernicus, N., *On the Revolutions of Heavenly Spheres*, 1543, tr. Wallis, C.G., p.5
9   Copernicus, N., *Commentariolus*, tr. Rosen, E., Osiris, Vol. III, 1938, p.126
10   Copernicus, N., *On the Revolutions of Heavenly Spheres*, tr. Wallis, C.G., p.26

11   Copernicus, N., *Commentariolus*, tr. Rosen, E., Osiris, Vol. III, 1938, p.126
12   Crowe, M.J., *Theories of the World from Antiquity to the Copernican Revolution*, 1990, pp.104-105
13   *Ibid.*, p.104

Chapter 4 THE SECRET OF THE PLANETS
1   Dreyer, J.L.E., *Tycho Brahe*, p.14
2   Brahe, T., *On a New Star*, extract reproduced in Shapley, E. and Howarth, H.E., *A Source Book in Astronomy*, 1929, p.13
3   Sagan, C. and Druyan, A., *Comet*, p.32
4   Brahe, T., *Op.Cit.*, p.13
5
6   Koyré, A., *The Astronomical Revolution*, 1973, p.162
7   Kepler, J., *New Astronomy*, tr. Donahue, W.H., 1992, p.184
8   Koestler, A., *Sleepwalkers*, 1959, p.280 and Caspar, M., *Kepler*, p.87
9   Kepler, J., *Op.Cit.*, p.185
10   Koestler, A., *Op.Cit.*, pp.308-309
11   Dreyer, J.L.E., *Op.Cit.*, pp.386-387
12   Kepler, J., *Op.Cit.*, p.286
13   *Ibid.*, p.543
14   *Ibid.*, p.78
15   Koyré, A., *Op.Cit.*, p.398
16   Caspar, M., *Op.Cit.*, p.206-207
17   *Ibid.*, pp.254-255
18   *Ibid.*, p.256
19   Kepler, J., *Harmonies of the World*, Book 5, Proem

Chapter 5 '…THE SHAPES OF CYNTHIA'
1   Galileo, G., *The Starry Messenger*, 1610, tr. Drake, S. in *Discoveries and Opinions of Galileo*, 1957, pp.28-29
2   *Ibid.*, pp.27-28
3   *Ibid.*, pp.29-30
4   *Ibid.*, p.51
5   *Ibid.*, p.53
6   *Ibid.*, p.57
7   Pannekoek, A., *A History of Astronomy*, p.230
8   Lattis, J.M., *Between Copernicus and Galileo: Christopher Clavius and the Collapse of Ptolemaic Astronomy*, pp.
9   Galileo, G., *Letter to the Grand Duchess Christina*, included in Drake, S., *Op.Cit.*, p.181
10   *Ibid.*, p.186
11   Drake,S., *Op.Cit.*, p.163
12   Gingerich, O., *The Great Copernicus Chase*, 1992, p.119
13   *Ibid.*, p.120

Chapter 6 ORBITS AND TRANSITS

1   Copernicus, N., *On the Revolutions of the Heavenly Spheres*, 1543, Vol. 1,
        10, tr. in Crowe,M.J., *Theories of the World from Antiquity to the Coperni-
        can Revolution*, p.129
2   Galileo, G., *Letter on Sunspots*, 1612, tr. Drake, S., in *Discoveries and
        Opinions of Galileo*, 1957, pp.94-95
3   Galileo, G., *Dialogue Concerning the Two Chief World Systems -
        Ptolemaic and Copernican*, 1632, tr. Drake, S., (UCP) 1967, p.339

Chapter 7 'A MOST AGREEABLE SPECTACLE'

1   Caspar,M., *Kepler*, (Dover edition, 1993), p.167
2   *Ibid.*, p.167
3   Gingerich,O., *The Great Copernicus Chase*, 1992, p.37
4   Stratton,F.J.M., *Horrox and the Transit of Venus*, Occasional Notes of the
        Royal Astronomical Society, No.7, 1939 December, p.90
5   Horrocks,J., *Venus in Sole Visa*, appended to Whatton,A.B., *Memoirs of the
        Life and Times of the Rev. Jeremiah Horrox*, 1859, p.109
6   *Ibid.*, pp.110-111
7   *Ibid.*, p.131
8   Stratton,F.J.M., *Op.Cit.*, p.92
9   Horrocks,J., *Op.Cit.*, p.126
10   *Ibid.*, pp.121-123
11   *Ibid.*, p.123
12   *Ibid.*, p.124
13   *Ibid.*, p.126
14   *Ibid.*, p.127
15   *Ibid.*, pp.128-129
16   *Ibid.*, p.129
17   *Ibid.*, p.202
18   *Ibid.*, p.212
19   Newton,I., *Principia Mathematica*, Motte's translation, revised by
        F.Cajori, Vol.2, Book 3, p.475
20   Whatton,A.B., *Op.Cit.*, p.58

Chapter 8 PREDICTING TRANSITS OF VENUS

1   Horrocks,J., *Op.Cit.*, 1859, p.135

Chapter 9 TO THE FOUR CORNERS OF THE EARTH

1   Brown, L.A., *The Story of Maps*, 1979, p.208
2   Howse, D., *Greenwich Time and the Longitude*, 1997, p.44
3   Blackburne Daniell, F.H., (ed), *Calendar of State Papers, Domestic Series,
        March 11th 1676 to February 28th 1677*, 1909, p.314

Chapter 10 HALLEY'S ADMONITION

1   Halley, E., *The Correspondence of Henry Oldenburg* (Eds. A.R. and M.B.
        Hall), 8 Aug 1776, Vol. XIII, p.27

2   Forbes, E.G., Murdin, L., and Willmoth, F. (Eds), *The Correspondence of John Flamsteed, The First Astronomer Royal*, Vol.1 (1666-1682),1995, Letter to Towneley, 8 June 1675, p.351

3   Bryant, A., *The Letters, Speeches and Declarations of King Charles II*, 1935, p.286

4   Cook, A., *Edmond Halley: Charting the Heavens and the Seas*, 1998, p.74

5   Halley, E., *A New Method of Determining the Parallax of the Sun, Abridged Transactions of the Royal Society*, 1716, p.244

6   Cook, A., *Op.Cit.*, p.80

7   Forbes, E.G., Murdin, L., and Willmoth, F. (Eds), *Op.Cit.*, p

8   Halley, E., *Op.Cit.*, translation given by J.Ferguson in *Astronomy Explained ... etc*, p.453

9   Halley, E., *On the Visible Conjunctions of the Inferior Planets with the Sun*, Abridged Transactions of the Royal Society, 1675, Vol. IX, p.197

10   Halley, E., *Op.Cit.*, translation given by J.Ferguson in *Astronomy Explained ... etc*, p.453-454

11   Picard, J., *Account of the Measure of the Earth's Meridian*, Abridged Transactions of the Royal Society, 1675, Vol. IX, p.197

12   Cook, A., *Op.Cit.*, p.172

13   *Ibid.*, p.172

14   Halley, E., *Op.Cit.*, p.455

15   *Ibid.*, pp.457-458

16   *Ibid.*, p.459

17   Cook, A., *Op.Cit.*, pp.403-404

Chapter 11 THE 1761 TRANSIT OF VENUS

1   Woolf,H., *The Transits of Venus: A Study of Eighteenth-Century Science*, Princeton University Press, 1959, p.73

2   *Ibid*, p.83

3   *Ibid*, p.89

4   *Ibid*, p.91

5   *Ibid*, p.92-93

6   Bradley,J., *Miscellaneous Works and Correspondence of the Rev.James Bradley* (ed. SP Rigaud), Oxford University Press, 1832, pp.388-390

7   Mason,C. and Dixon,J., *Observations made at the Cape of Good Hope*, Philosophical Transactions of the Royal Society, Vol.52, Dec.1761,p.384

8   Maskelyne,N., *An Account of the Observations made on the Transit of Venus, June 6, 1761, in the Island of St.Helena*, Philosophical Transactions of the Royal Society, Vol.52, Dec.1761,pp.196-198

9   Woolf,H., *Op.Cit.*, pp.100-101

10   Bertrand,J., *L'Académie des Sciences et les Académiciens de 1666 à 1793*, J.Hetzel, 1869, p.137

11   Pingré,A-G, *Observations Astronomiques pour la Détermination de la Parallaxe du Soleil, Faites en l'Isle Rodrigue*, Memoires de l'Académie Royale des Sciences, 1761, p.414

12   Pingré,A-G, Philosophical Transactions of the Royal Society, Vol.60, Dec.1770,pp.500-501

13 Chappe d'Auteroche,J-B., *A Journey into Siberia made by Order of the King of France*, 1768, quoted in *The 1769 Transit of Venus: The Baja California Observations of Jean-Baptiste Chappe-d'Auteroche, etc*, by Doyce B.Nunis Jr, Natural History Museum of Los Angeles County, 1982, pp.32-34

14 Chappe d'Auteroche, *Extrait du Voyage fait en Sibérie, pour l'Observation de Vénus sur le disque du Soleil, faite à Tobolsk le 6 Juin 1761*, Mémoires de l'Académie Royale des Sciences, 1769, p.345

15 Chappe d'Auteroche,J-B., quoted in Nunis, *op.cit.*, p.34

16 Chappe d'Auteroche,J-B., quoted in Nunis, *op.cit*, p.36

17 Halley,E., *A new Method of determining the Parallax of the Sun*, Abridged Transactions of the Royal Society, Vol. XXIX, 1716, p.246

18 Maskelyne,N., *Op.Cit.*, p199-200

Chapter 12 'HAPPY IS OUR CENTURY'

1 Pingré,A-G, quoted in *The Transits of Venus: A Study of Eighteenth-Century Science*, by Harry Woolf, Princeton University Press, 1959, p.153 (tr. DS)

2 Le Gentil, G., *Voyages dans les mer de l'Indes, etc*, tr. and quoted by Helen Sawyer Hogg, *Out of Old Books*, Journal of the Royal Astronomical Society of Canada, Vol XLV, 1951, p.90

3 *Ibid*, p.130

4 *Ibid*, p.131

5 *Ibid*, p.131

6 Le Gentil,G., quoted in Woolf,H., *Op.Cit.*, p.155 (tr. DS)

7 Chappe-d'Auteroche,J-B., quoted in *The 1769 Transit of Venus: The Baja California Observations of Jean-Baptiste Chappe-d'Auteroche, etc*, by Doyce B.Nunis Jr, Natural History Museum of Los Angeles County, 1982, p.65

8 Cassini, C-F, quoted by Nunis, op cit, pp.75-76

9 de Fouchy, G., *Éloge de M. l'Abbé Chappe*, Histoire de l'Académie Royale des Sciences, 1769, p.171

10 de Fouchy, G., quoted by Angus Armitage in *Chappe d'Auteroche: A Pathfinder for Astronomy*, Annals of Science, Vol 10,No.4, Dec 1954, p.293

11 Pingré,A-G., *A Letter from M.Pingré, of the Royal Academy of Sciences at Paris, to the Rev.Mr.Maskelyne, Astronomer Royal*, Philosophical Transactions of the Royal Society, Vol 60, Dec.1770, pp.498-499

12 Airy,G.B., *On the means which will be available for correcting the measure of the Sun's distance, in the next twenty-five Years*, Monthly Notices of the Royal astronomical Society, Vol XVII, 1857, p.209

13 Newcomb,S., *On Hell's alleged Falsification of his Observations ..*, Monthly Notices of the Royal Astronomical Society, Vol XLIII, 1883,pp.370-381

14 Newcomb,S., *The Reminiscences of an Astronomer*, Harper & Brothers, 1903, p.160

15 *Ibid*, pp.158-159

16   Hornsby,T., *On the Transit of Venus in 1769*, Abridged Transactions of the Royal Society, Vol XII, 1776, p.274

17   *Ibid*, p.273

18   Bevis,J., *An Observation of an Eclipse of the Sun at the Island of New-found-land, August 5, 1766, by Mr.James Cook, with the Longitude of the Place of Observation deduced from it*, Philosophical Transactions of the Royal Society, Vol

19   Short,J., *Second Paper concerning the Parallax of the Sun, etc,* , Abridged Transactions of the Royal Society, Vol LIII, 1763,pp.28-29

20   Wallis,S., quoted by Fernie,D. in *The Whisper and the Vision: The Voyages of the Astronomers*, Clarke,Irwin & Co, 1976, p.27

21   Cartier,J., quoted by Kodicek,E.H. and Young,F.G. in *Captain Cook and Scurvey*, Notes and Records of the Royal Society, Vol 24, 1969, p.44

22   Kodicek,E.H. and Young,F.G, *Op.Cit.*, p.60

23   Cook,J., *The Journals of Captain James Cook on his Voyages of Discovery. Vol 1: The Voyage of the Endeavour: 1768-1771*, 3 June 1769, Ed. Beaglehole, J.C., pp.97-98

24   *Ibid*, p.99

25   *Ibid*, p.98

26   Cook,J., *Observations made, by appointment of the Royal Society, at King George's Island in the South Sea; by Mr.Charles Green, formerly Assistant at the Royal Observatory at Greenwich, and Lieut.James Cook, of his Majesty's Ship the Endeavour*, Philosophical Transactions of the Royal Society, Vol 61, 1771, p.410-411

27   Cook,J., *Op.Cit.*, 29 Jan 1771, p.172

28   Hornsby,T., *The Quantity of the Sun's Parallax as deduced from the Observations of the Transit of Venus, on June 3, 1769*, Philosophical Transactions of the Royal Society, Vol 61, 1771, p.579

29   Cassini,C.F., quoted by Woolf,H., *op.cit*, p.22 (tr DS)

30   Hornsby,T., *Op.Cit.*, p.574

Chapter 13 VENUS ABANDONED

1   Grant, R., *History of Physical Astronomy*, 1885, p.212

2   Turner,H.H.., *Modern Astronomy*, 1901, p.96

3   Newcomb,S., *Discussion of Observations of the Transits of Venus in 1761 and 1769*, Astronomical Papers prepared for the Use of the American Ephemeris and Nautical Almanac, 1891, p.263

4   *Ibid*, p.263

5   *Ibid*, p.264

6   Tupman, Cpt.G.L., *On the Photographs of the Transit of Venus*, Monthly Notices of the RAS, Vol38, 1878, p.509

7   Brück,H.A. and M.T., *The Peripatetic Astronomer: The Life of Charles Piazzi Smyth*, p.88

8   Gill, D., *A History and Description of the Royal Observatory, Cape of Good Hope*, 1913, p.xxxi

9   *Ibid*, p.xxxii

10   Eastman, J.R., *A Value of the Solar Parallax from Meridian Observations of Mars at the Opposition in 1877*, 1881, p.7

11   Gill,I., *Six Months in Ascension: An Unscientific Account of a Scientific Expedition*, 1878, Ch.1

12   *Ibid*, Ch.1

13   *Ibid*, Ch.4

14   *Ibid*, Ch.7

15   *Ibid*, Ch.7

16   Forbes,E.G., Murdin,L. and Willmoth,F. (Eds), *The Correspondence of John Flamsteed, The First Astronomer Royal*, Vol.1 (1666-1682), Letter to Oldenburg, 16 November 1672, p.185

17   Halley,E., *A New Method of determining the Parallax of the Sun, or his Distance from the Earth*, Abridged Transactions of the Royal Society, 1716, Vol 6, p.244

18   Gingerich,O., *The Great Copernicus Chase*, 1992, p.252

19   Airy,G.B., *On the Means which will be available for correcting the Measure of the Sun's Distance in the next twenty-five Years*, Monthly Notices of the Royal Astronomical Society, Vol.XVII, 1857, p.220

Chapter 14 VENUS RECLAIMED

1   Linke,F., *Kosmos*, Dec 1948, quoted by Ley,W., *Watchers of the Skies*, 1964, pp.324-325

2   Newcomb,S., *Usefulness of the Planet DQ for determining the Solar Parallax*, The Astronomical Journal, Vol 19, 22 Nov 1898, pp.147-8

3   Spencer Jones, H., *The Distance of the Sun*, Endeavour, Vol.1, Jan 1942, p.17

4   Butrica, A.J., *To See the Unseen:A History of Planetary Radar Astronomy*, NASA, 1996, p.32

5   *Ibid.*, p.33

6   Green, P.E. and Pettengill, G.H., *Exploring the Solar System by Radar*, Sky and Telescope, 20, 1960, p.13, quoted in Butrica, A.J., Op.Cit., p36

7   Butrica, A.J., *Op.Cit.*, p.36

8   Pettengill, G.H., *Radar Astronomy* (Eds. Evans, J.V. and Hagfors,T.), MIT Lincoln Laboratory/McGraw Hill, 1968, p.284

9   Butrica, A.J., *Op.Cit.*, p.40

10   Shapiro,I.I., *Radar Observations of the Planets*, Scientific American, July 1968, Vol.219, No.1, p.29

11   Turnbull,H.W., The Correspondence of Isaac Newton, Vol.1, Cambridge, 1959, Letter 154 (5 February 1675/76), p.416

Chapter 15 THE COMING TRANSITS OF 2004 AND 2012

1   Harkness, W., *On the Transits of Venus*, Nature, 30 Nov 1882, p.114

2   Goldstein, B.R., *Some Medieval Reports of Venus and Mercury Transits*, Centaurus, Vol. 14, 1969, pp.49-50

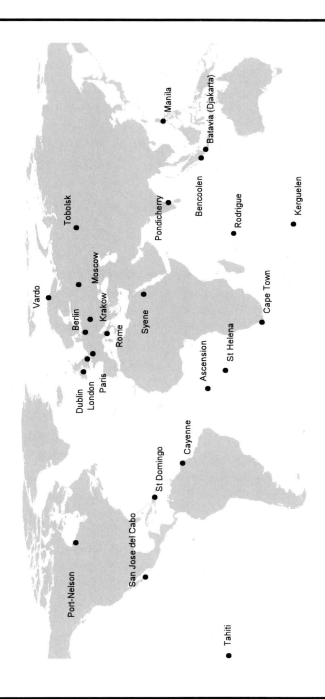

Map of Key Places

The Solar Parallax and the Sun's Distance

| Solar Parallax (arc-secs) | Mean Distance of the Sun | | | ** |
	In Earth-radii	Miles *	Kilometres *	
180	1,146	4,541,606	7,308,808	Ptolemy
60	3,438	13,624,821	21,926,430	Kepler
14	14,733	58,392,093	93,970,415	Horrocks
13.5	15,279	60,554,763	97,450,801	
13	15,867	62,883,793	101,198,908	
12.5	16,501	65,399,144	105,246,865	
12	17,189	68,124,109	109,632,151	
11.5	17,936	71,086,027	114,398,766	
11	18,751	74,317,210	119,598,710	
10.5	19,644	77,856,124	125,293,887	
10	20,626	81,748,931	131,558,581	
9.5	21,712	86,051,506	138,482,717	
9	22,918	90,832,145	146,176,201	
8.8	23,439	92,896,512	149,498,388	Spencer Jones (1931)
8.794148	23,455	92,958,329	149,597,870	Present Day - IAU (1976)
8.794	23,455	92,959,894	149,600,388	IAU (1964)
8.790	23,466	93,002,196	149,668,465	Newcomb (1891), IAU (pre-1964)
8.780	23,493	93,108,121	149,838,931	Gill (1877)
8.577	24,049	95,311,800	153,385,311	Encke (1825)
8.5	24,266	96,175,212	154,774,801	
8	25,783	102,186,163	164,448,226	
7.5	27,502	108,998,574	175,411,441	

* Assuming that the Equatorial Radius of the Earth is 6,378.140 kilometres (3,963.30 miles)—International Astronomical Union (IAU) 1976.
** Names relate to the solar parallax. The distance of the Sun would have been based on value for the Earth radius current at the time.

FURTHER READING

The main purpose of this book is to show how it is possible to know something as intangible as the distance of the Sun. It tries to explain, as far as possible, exactly what astronomers have seen, which convinces them that they know the distance. In order to fulfill this purpose, I have selected episodes from the history of astronomy (and geography) which seem to be pivotal to the explanation and intrinsically interesting. At the same time, I have tried to limit myself to recounting only what is sufficient for that purpose. I have therefore omitted items which, judged in this light, would simply be duplication.

In adopting this approach, I am conscious that I could be accused of being too selective. In particular, the approach adopted has resulted in the book omitting mention of many astronomers who have justly earned a place in the history of attempts to determine the solar parallax and the figure of the Earth. My excuse is that, this is not intended to be an exhaustive, scholarly treatise on the subject: merely a 'story'. It is a story however, which, hopefully even at this simple level, lifts our eyes to the grandest of subjects – our place in the Solar System.

My initial interest in the Transit of Venus was aroused by a 1994 BBC Television programme—*Heavenly Bodies*—which gave a reconstruction of Horrocks' 1639 observation. This interest was soon dampened when I discovered that the topic did not seem to be covered in detail by popular astronomy texts, or indeed by any books currently in print. The reader whose appetite is whet by the present offering will need to forage through many a dusty old volume to find out more. Many of the sources of information will only be found in University Libraries, or on the archive stacks of Public Libraries. Complete scanned images of old journals are starting to become available on the World Wide Web—for example, *the Internet Library of Early Journals* (www.bodley.ox.ac.uk/ilej) and the marvelous *Gallica* site of the French National Library (gallica.bnf.fr). To assist the undaunted, I list below some of the sources which I have found most useful:

Chapter 1: Prologue: Dublin, 1882
Ball,R.S., *The Story of the Heavens*, Cassell, 1886
O'Hora,N.P.J., *The Dunsink Observatory*, The Observatory, Vol.81,1961,pp189-195
Dreyer,J.L.E., *Sir Robert Ball,FRS*, Nature, 4 Dec 1913, pp403-404
The Times, 7 Dec 1882
Wayman,P.A., *Dunsink Observatory, 1785-1985: A Bicentennial History*, Royal Dublin Society, 1987

Chapter 2: Wandering Stars
Ball,W.V., *Reminiscences and Letters of Sir Robert Ball*, Cassell, 1915
Cortie,A.L., *Father Perry, FRS: The Jesuit Astronomer*, Catholic Truth Society,1890
Heath,T.L., *Aristarchus of Samos: The Ancient Copernicus*, Dover, 1981 (original, 1913)
Heath,T.L., *Greek Astronomy*, Dent,1932 (Dover reprint, 1991)
Perry,S.J., *The Transit of Venus*, Royal Institution Library of Science: Astronomy, Vol.1, 1970,pp153-159 (original, 1876)
Proceedings of the Royal Society, *Sir Robert Stawell Ball,1840-1913*, Series A,Vol.XCI, Sept 1915
Shapley, H. and Howarth,E.H. (Eds), *A Sourcebook in Astronomy*, McGraw-Hill, 1929

Chapter 3: Heavenly Spheres
Aristotle, *On the Heavens*, tr. W.K.C.Guthrie, The Loeb Classical Library, Harvard UP/Heinemann, 1939
Armitage,A., *The World of Copernicus*, EP Publishing, 1972
Copernicus,N., *On the Revolutions of the Heavenly Spheres,* tr. A.M.Duncan, David & Charles, also, tr.G.C.Glenn, Prometheus Books, 1995
Copernicus,N., *Commentariolus*, tr.Edward Rosen, Osiris, Vol.III, St Catherine Press Ltd, 1938
Crowe,M.J., *Theories of the World from Antiquity to the Copernican Revolution*, Dover, 1990
Gingerich,O., *The Eye of Heaven: Ptolemy, Copernicus, Kepler*, American Institute of Physics, 1993
Gingerich,O., *The Great Copernicus Chase*, Cambridge University Press, 1992
Kesten,H., *Copernicus and his World*, Secker & Warburg, 1945

Kuhn,T.S., *The Copernican Revolution*, Harvard University Press, 1957 (reprinted 1997)

Ptolemy,C., *Ptolemy's Almagest*, tr. Toomer,G.J., Princeton University Press, 1998

Rosen,E.,.,(Ed), *Three Copernican Treatises: The Commentariolus, The Letter against Werner, The Narratio prima*, Columbia University Press, 1939

Rudnicki,J., *Nicholas Copernicus*, Copernicus Quartercentenary Celebration Committee, 1943

Sambursky,S., *Physical Thought from the Presocratics to the Quantum Physicists: An Anthology*, Hutchinson, 1974

Thurston,H., *Early Astronomy*, Springer, 1996

Chapter 4: The Secret of the Planets

Beer,A.& P., (Eds), *Kepler: 400 years*, Vistas in Astronomy, Vol.18, 1975

Brahe,T., *On a New Star*, extract in A Sourcebook in Astronomy (see above)

Caspar,M., *Kepler*, Dover, 1993 (original, 1948)

Gade,J.A., *The Life and Times of Tycho Brahe*, Princeton University Press, 1947

Kepler,J., *New Astronomy*, tr. W.H.Donahue, Cambridge University Press, 1992

Kepler,J., *The Epitome of Copernican Astronomy & Harmonies of the World*, tr.C.G.Glenn, Prometheus Books, 1995

Koestler,A., *The Sleepwalkers*, Penguin, 1986 (original, 1959)

Koyré ,A., *The Astronomical Revolution*, Methuen, 1973 (original, 1961)

Thoren,V.E., *The Lord of Uraniborg: A Biography of Tycho Brahe*, Cambridge University Press, 1990

Chapter 5: '... The Shapes of Cynthia'

Drake,S., (tr), *Discoveries and Opinions of Galileo*, (incl. The Starry Messenger (1610), Letter to the Grand Duchess Christina (1615)), Anchor, 1957

Galileo,G., *Dialogue Concerning the Two Chief World Systems*, University of California, 1967 (original, 1630)

Chapter 6: Orbits and Transits

Kaler,J.B., *The Ever-Changing Sky: A Guide to the Celestial Sphere*, Cambridge University Press, 1996

Chapter 7:'A Most Agreeable Spectacle'

Barocas, V., *A Country Curate*, Qtly Jnl RAS, Vol.12, 1971, pp179-182

Beaulieu,A., *L'énigmatique Gassendi: prévôt et Savant*, Académie des Sciences, La Vie des Sciences, Vol.9, No.3, 1992, pp205-229

Bulpit,W.T., *Misconceptions concerning Jeremiah Horrocks, the Astronomer*, The Observatory, Vol.XXXVII, Sept 1914, pp335-337

Chapman,A., *Jeremiah Horrocks, the transit of Venus, and the 'New Astronomy' in early seventeenth-century England*, Qtly Jnl RAS, Vol.31, 1990, pp333-357

Gaythorpe,S.B., *Horrocks's Observations of the Transit of Venus, 1639 November 24 (O.S.)*, Jnl of BAA, Dec 1936, pp60-68 and Jul 1954, pp309-315

Plummer,H.C., *Jeremiah Horrocks and his Opera Posthuma*, Notes and Records of the Royal Society, Vol.3, pp39-52, London, 1940-41

Stratton,F.J.M., *Horrox and the Transit of Venus*, Occasional Notes of the R.A.S., No.7, Dec 1939, pp89-95

Van Helden,A., *Measuring the Universe: Cosmic Dimensions from Aristarchus to Halley*, Chicago University Press, 1985

Van Helden,A., *The Importance of the Transit of Mercury of 1631*, Jnl for the History of Astronomy, Vol.7, 1976, pp1-10

Whatton,A.B., *Memoir of the Life and Times of the Rev.Jeremiah Horrox (incl. Venus in Sole Visa)*, Wertheim, Macintosh and Hunt, 1859

Wilson,C., *Astronomy from Kepler to Newton*, Vaporium Reprints, 1989, ch VI

Chapter 8: Predicting Transits of Venus
Meeus,J., *The Transits of Venus: 3000BC to AD3000*, Jnl of BAA, Vol.68, 1958, pp98-108

Porter,J.G., *Transits of Mercury & Venus*, Jnl of BAA, Vol.80, 3, 1970, pp182-189

Proctor,R.A., *Essays on Astronomy*, Longmans, Green & Co., 1872

Proctor,R.A., *Transits of Venus: A Popular Account of Past and Coming Transits*, Longmans, Green & Co., 1874

Chapter 9: To the Four Corners of the Earth
Brown,L.A., *The Story of Maps*, Dover, 1979 (original, 1949)

Howse,D., *Greenwich Time and the Longitude*, Philip Wilson, 1997

Maunder,E.W., *The Royal Observatory Greenwich: A Glance at its History and Work*, The Religious Tract Society, 1900

Olmsted,J.W., *The Scientific Expedition of Jean Richer to Cayenne (1672-73)*, Isis, Vol XXXIV, 1942-43, pp117-128

Turner,G.L'E., *Scientific Instruments: 1500-1900*, Philip Wilson, 1998

Williams,J.E.D., *From Sails to Satellites: the Origin and Development of Navigational Science*, Oxford University Press, 1994

Chapter 10: Halley's Admonition
Armitage,A., *Edmond Halley*, Nelson, 1966

Cook,A. *Edmond Halley: Charting the Heavens and the Seas*, Oxford University Press, 1998

Forbes,E.G.,Murdin,L., and Willmoth,F. (Eds), *The Correspondence of John Flamsteed, the First Astronomer Royal*, Institute of Physics, 1995

Hall,A.R. & M.B., (Eds) *The Correspondence of Henry Oldenburg*, Vols XII and XIII, Taylor & Francis, 1986

Halley,E., *On the Visible Conjunction of the inferior Planets with the Sun*, Abgd Trans of RS, 1691, pp448-456

Halley,E., *A new Method of determining the Parallax of the Sun, or his Distance from the Earth*, Abgd Trans of RS, 1716, pp243-249

Levallois,J.-J., *L'Académie Royale des Sciences et la Figure de la Terre*, Académie des Sciences, La Vie des Sciences, Comptes Rendus, Vol.3, General Series No.3, May-Jun 1986, pp261-301

Norwood,R., *Advertisement concerning the Quantity of a Degree of a great Circle, in English Measures*, Abgd Trans of RS, 1676, pp305-307

Picard,J., *Account of the Measure of the Earth's Meridian*, Abgd Trans of RS, 1675, pp193-198

Turnbull,H.W. (Ed), *James Gregory Tercentenary Memorial Volume*, G.Bell & Sons, 1939

Waters,D.W., *The Art of Navigation in England in Elizabethan and Early Stuart Times*, Holland & Carter, 1958

Chapter 11: The 1761 Transit of Venus

Armitage,A., *Chappe d'Auteroche: A Pathfinder for Astronomy*, Annals of Science, Vol.10, No.4, Dec 1954, pp277-293

Bliss,N., *A Second Account of the Transit of Venus over the Sun*, June 6 1761, Abgd Trans of RS, 1761, pp564-570

Chappe d'Auteroche,J-B, *Extrait du Voyage fait en Siberie Pour l'Observation de Venus sur le disque du Soleil, faite à Tobolsk le 6 Juin 1761*, Memoires de l'Academie des Sciences, 13 Nov 1762

Ferguson,J., *Astronomy Explained Upon Sir Isaac Newton's Principles, etc*, London, 1772

Hornsby,T., *On the Parallax of the Sun*, Abgd Trans of RS, 1763, pp44-60

Howse,D., *Nevil Maskelyne: The Seaman's Astronomer*, Cambridge, 1989

Lalande,J-J de, *Memoire sur les Passages de Venus devant le Disque du Soleil en 1761 et 1769*, Memoires de l'Academie des Sciences, 14 May 1760

Le Gentil, G., *Memoire de M. Le Gentil … au sujet de l'Observation qu'il va faire, par ordre du Roi, dans les Indes Orientale, du prochain passage de Venus pardevant le Soleil*, Journal des Sçavans, March 1760, pp132-142

Maskelyne,N., *An Account of the Observations made on the Transit of Venus, June 6, 1761, in the Island of St.Helena*, Phil.Trans. of RS, Vol 52, Dec 1761, pp196-201

Mason,C. and Dixon,J., *Observations made at the Cape of Good Hope*, Phil Trans of RS, Vol 52, Dec 1761

Milburn,J.R., *Wheelwright of the Heavens: The Life and Work of James Ferguson, FRS*, Vade-Mecum Press, 1988

Pingré ,A.-G., *Observation of the Transit of Venus over the Sun, June 6, 1761, at the Island of Rodrigues*, Phil Trans of RS, Vol 52, Dec 1761, pp371-377

Short,J., *The Observations of the Internal Contact of Venus with the Sun's limb, etc*, Abgd Trans of RS, 1762, pp649-660

Short,J., *Second Paper concerning the Parallax of the Sun determined from the Observations of the late Transit of Venus, etc*, Abgd Trans of RS, 1763, pp22-37

Woolf,H., *Eighteenth-Century Observations of the Transits of Venus*, Annals of Science, Vol.9, 1953, pp.176-190

Woolf,H., *The Transits of Venus: A Study of Eighteenth-century Science*, Princeton University Press, 1959

Chapter 12: "Happy is Our Century"

Academie Royale des Sciences, *Eloge de M.l'Abbé Chappe*, Histoire de l'Academie Royales des Sciences, 1769, pp163-172

Armitage,A., *The Pilgrimage of Pingré*, Annals of Science, Vol.9, 1953, pp.47-63

Beaglehole,J.C., *The Life of Captain James Cook*, Stanford University Press, 1974

Fernie,D., *The Whisper and the Vision: The Voyages of the Astronomers*, Clarke, Irwin & Co, 1976, pp8-17,26-31,40-51

Ferrer,Don José Joaquin de, *On the Determination of the Parallax of the Sun from the Observations of the Transit of Venus over his disk, June 3,1769*, Memoirs of the RAS, Vol.V, 1833, pp.253-296

Green,C. and Cook,J., *Observations made by appointment of the Royal Society at King George's Island in the South Sea*, Phil Trans of RS, Vol 61, 1771, pp397-421

Hindle,B., *David Rittenhouse*, Princeton University Press, 1964

Hogg,H.S., *Out of Old Books, Le Gentil and the Transits of Venus, 1761 and 1769*, Jnl of RAS of Canada, Vol XLV (1951), pp.37-44,89-93,127-134,173-178

Hornsby,T., *The Quantity of the Sun's Parallax, as deduced from the Observations of the Transit of Venus, on June 3, 1769*, Phil Trans of RS, Vol.61, 1771, pp574-579

Morton,A.Q. and Weiss,J.A., *Public & Private Science: The King George III Collection*, Oxford University Press, 1993, pp27-29, 116-117

Newcomb,S., *On Hell's alleged Falsification of his Observations of the Transit of Venus in 1769*, Monthly Notices of the RAS, Vol.XLIII, 1883, pp371-381

Newcomb,S., *Reminiscences of an Astronomer*, Harper and Brothers, 1903, pp.151-181

Nunis, D.B.,Jnr., *The 1769 Transit of Venus: The Baja California Observations of Jean-Baptiste Chappe-d'Auteroche*, Natural History Museum of Los Angeles County, 1982

Pingré ,A.-G., *A Letter from M.Pingré ... to the Rev.Mr.Maskelyne ...*, Phil Trans of RS, Vol 60, Dec 1770, pp497-501

Sarton,G., *Vindication of Father Hell*, ISIS, Vol.XXXV, Pt.2, No.100, Spring 1944, pp97-105

Westfall,J.E., *The 1769 Transit of Venus Expedition to San José del Cabo*, Research Amateur Astronomy, ASP Conference Series, Vol.33, 1992, pp.234-242

Wooley,R., *Captain Cook and the Transit of Venus of 1769*, Notes and Records of the RS, Vol.24, 1969, pp19-32

Chapter 13: Venus Abandoned

Airy,G.B., *On the Means which will be available for correcting the Measure of the Sun's Distance in the next twenty-five Years*, Monthly Notices of RAS, Vol XVII, 1857, pp.208-221

Brück, H.A. and M.T., *The Peripatetic Astronomer: The Life of Charles Piazzi Smyth*, Adam Hilger

Dreyer,J.L.E. and Turner,H.H., (Eds), *History of the Royal Astronomical Society*, Vol 1, Blackwell, 1987 (original 1923)

Eastman,J.R., *A Value of the Solar Parallax from Meridian Observations of Mars at the Opposition in 1877*, Government Printing Office, Washington, 1881

Gill,D., *Reports on the Expedition to Ascension*, Monthly Notices of RAS, Vol 38, 1878,

Gill,D., *A History and Description of the Royal Observatory, Cape of Good Hope*, HMSO, 1913

Gill,I., *Six Months in Ascension: An Unscientific Account of a Scientific Expedition*, John Murray, 1878

Grant,R., *History of Physical Astronomy*, Henry G. Bohn, 1885

Lankford,J., *Photography and the 19th Century Transits of Venus*, Technology and Culture, Vol 28, No.3, Jul 1987, pp648-657

Newcomb,S., *Astronomical Papers prepared for the use of the American Ephemeris and Nautical Almanac (Vol.II)*, US Navy Department, 1891

Newcomb,S., *Popular Astronomy*, Macmillan, 1883

Proceedings of the Royal Society, *Sir David Gill, KCB, 1843-1914*, Series A, Vol.XCI (September 1915)

Stone,E.J., *A Rediscussion of the Observations of the Transit of Venus, 1769*, Monthly Notices of RAS, Vol XXVIII, 1868, pp255-266

Chapter 14: Venus Reclaimed

Buderi,R., *The Invention that changed the World: The Story of Radar from War to Peace*, Little Brown & Co, 1997

Butrica,A.J., *To See the Unseen: A History of Planetary Radar Astronomy*, NASA, 1996

Evans,J.V. and Hagfors,T., (Eds), *Radar Astronomy*, MIT Lincoln Laboratory/McGraw-Hill, 1968

Kahrstedt,A., *G.Witt*, Astronomische Nachrichten, Vol 276, Jan-Oct , Berlin, 1948, p192

Ley,W., *Watchers of the Skies*, Sidgwick & Jackson, 1964,pp317-338

Muhleman,D.O., Holdbridge,D.B. and Block,N., *The Astronomical Unit Determined by Radar Reflections from Venus*, The Astronomical Journal, Vol 67, No.4, May 1962, pp191-203

Pettengill,G. and Price,R., *Radar Echoes from Venus and a New Determination of the Solar Parallax*, Planetary & Space Science, Vol.5, pp.71–74

Spencer Jones,H., *The Solar Parallax and the Mass of the Moon from Observations of Eros at the Opposition of 1931*, Monthly Notices of RAS, Vol 101, 1941, pp356-366

Spencer Jones,H., *The distance of the Sun*, Endeavour, Vol.1, Jan 1942

Van Biesbroeck,G., *The Coming Opposition of Eros*, Popular Astronomy, Vol XXXVIII, No.10, Dec 1930, pp575-579

Chapter 15: The Coming Transits of 2004 and 2012

Goldstein,B.R., *Some Medieval Reports of Venus and Mercury Transits*, Centaurus, Vol.14, 1969 (source of Honolulu Commercial Advertiser quote)

Harkness,W., *On the Transits of Venus*, Nature, 30 Nov 1882, pp114-117

Meeus,J., *Transits*, Willmann-Bell, 1989

EDMOND HALLEY'S FAMOUS EXHORTATION OF 1716

With explanatory footnotes by James Ferguson, FRS

Doctor HALLEY'S *Dissertation on the method of finding the Sun's parallax and distance from the Earth, by the Transit of Venus over the Sun's Disc,* June *the 6th,* 1761. *Translated from the Latin in* Motte's *Abridgment of the Philosophical Transactions, Vol. I. page* 243; *with additional notes.*

There are many things exceedingly paradoxical, and that seem quite incredible to the illiterate, which yet by means of mathematical principles may be easily solved. Scarce any problem will appear more hard and difficult, than that of determining the distance of the Sun from the Earth very near the truth: but even this, when we are made acquainted with some exact observations, taken at places fixed upon, and chosen beforehand, will without much labour be effected. And this is what I am now desirous to lay before this illustrious Society* (which I foretell will continue for ages) that I may explain before-hand to young Astronomers, who may perhaps live to observe these things, a method by which the immense distance of the Sun may be truly obtained, to within a five hundredth part of what it really is.

It is well known that the distance of the Sun from the Earth is by different Astronomers supposed different, according to what was judged most probable from the best conjecture that each would form. *Ptolemy* and his followers, as also *Copernicus* and *Tycho Brahe,* thought it to be 1200 semidiameters of the Earth: *Kepler* 3500 nearly: *Ricciolus* doubles the distance mentioned by *Kepler,* and *Hevelius* only increases it by one half. But the planets Venus and Mercury having, by the assistance of the telescope, been seen in the disc of

---

* The Royal Society

---

the Sun, deprived of their borrowed brightness, it is at length found that the apparent diameter of the planets are much less than they were formerly supposed; and that the semidiameter of Venus seen from the Sun subtends no more than a fourth part of a minute, or fifteen seconds, while the semidiameter of Mercury, at its mean distance from the Sun, is seen under an angle only of ten seconds; that the semidiameter of Saturn seen from the Sun appears under the same angle; and that the semidiameter of Jupiter, the largest of all the planets, subtends an angle of no more than a third part of a minute at the Sun. Whence, keeping the proportion, some modern Astronomers have thought, that the semidiameter of the Earth, seen from the Sun, would subtend a mean angle between that larger one subtended by Jupiter, and that smaller one subtended by Saturn and Mercury; and equal to that subtended by Venus (namely, fifteen seconds): and have thence concluded, that the Sun is distant from the Earth almost 14000 of the Earth's semidiameters. But the same authors have on another account somewhat increased this distance: for, inasmuch as the Moon's diameter is a little more than a fourth part of the diameter of the Earth, if the Sun's parallax should be supposed fifteen seconds, it would follow, that the body of the Moon is larger than that of Mercury; that is, that a secondary planet would be greater than a primary, which would seem inconsistent with the uniformity of the mundane system. And on the contrary, the same regularity and uniformity seems scarcely to admit, that Venus, an inferior planet, that has no satellite, should be greater than our Earth, which stands higher in the system, and has such a splendid attendant. Therefore, to observe a mean, let us suppose the semidiameter of the Earth seen from the Sun, or, which is the same thing, the Sun's horizontal parallax, to be twelve seconds and a half; according to which, the Moon will be less than Mercury, and the Earth larger than Venus; and the Sun's distance from the Earth will come out nearly 16,500 of the Earth's semidiameters. This distance I assent to at present, as the true one, till it shall become certain what it is, by the Experiment which I propose. Nor am I induced to alter my opinion by the authority of those (however weighty it may be) who are for placing the Sun at an immense distance beyond the bounds here assigned, relying on observations made upon the vibrations of a pendulum, in order to determine those exceeding small angles; but which, as it seems, are not sufficient to be depended upon: at least, by this method of investigating the parallax, it will come out sometimes nothing, or even negative; that is, the distance would either become infinite, or greater than infinite; which is absurd. And indeed, to confess the truth, it is hardly possible for a man to distinguish, with any degree of certainty, seconds, or even ten seconds, with instruments, let them be ever so skillfully made: therefore, it is not at all to be wondered at, that the excessive nicety of this matter has eluded the many and ingenious endeavours of such skilful operators.

About forty years ago, while I was in the island of *St. Helena*, observing the stars about the south pole, I had an opportunity of observing, with the greatest diligence, Mercury passing over the disc of the Sun; and (which succeeded better than I could have hoped for) I observed, with the greatest degree of accuracy, by means of a telescope 24 feet long, the very moment when Mercury entering upon the Sun seemed to touch its limb within, and also the moment when going off it struck the limb of the Sun's disc, forming the angle of interior contact: whence I found the interval of time, during which Mercury then appeared within the Sun's disc, even without an error of one second of time. For the lucid line intercepted between the dark limb of the planet and the bright limb of the Sun, although exceeding fine, is seen by the eye; and the little dent made in the Sun's limb, by Mercury's entering the disc, appears to vanish in a moment; and also that made by Mercury, when leaving the disc, seems to begin in an instant.—When I perceived this, it immediately came into my mind, that the Sun's parallax might be accurately determined by such kind of observations as these; provided Mercury were but nearer to the Earth, and had a greater parallax from the Sun: but the difference of these parallaxes is so little, as always to be less than the solar parallax which we seek; and therefore Mercury, though frequently to be seen on the Sun, is not to be looked upon as fit for our purpose.

There remains then the transit of Venus over the Sun's disc; whose parallax, being almost four times as great as the solar parallax, will cause very sensible differences between the times in which Venus will seem to be passing over the Sun at different parts of the Earth. And from these differences, if they be observed as they ought, the Sun's parallax may be determined even to a small part of a second. Nor do we require any other instruments for this purpose, than common telescopes and clocks, only good of their kind; and in the observers, nothing more is needful than fidelity, diligence, and a moderate skill in Astronomy. For there is no need that the latitude of the place should be scrupulously observed, nor that the hours themselves should be accurately determined with respect to the meridian: it is sufficient that the clocks be regulated according to the motion of the heavens, if the times be well reckoned from the total ingress of Venus into the Sun's disc, to the beginning of her egress from it; that is, when the dark globe of Venus first begins to touch the bright limb of the Sun within; which moments, I know by my own experience, may be observed within a second of time.

But on account of the very strict laws by which the motions of the planets are regulated, Venus is seldom seen within the Sun's disc: and during the course of more than 120 years, it could not be seen once; namely, from the year 1639 (when this most pleasing sight happened to that excellent youth, *Horrox*, our countryman, and to him only, since the creation) to the year 1761; in which year, according to the theories which we have hitherto found agreeable to the celestial motions, Venus will again pass over the Sun on the 26th of *May**, in the morning; so that at *London*, about six o'clock in the morning, we may expect to see it near the middle of the Sun's disc, and not above four minutes of a degree south of the Sun's center. But the duration of this transit will be almost eight hours; namely, from two o'clock in the morning till almost ten. Hence the ingress will not be visible in *England*; but as the Sun will at that time be in the 16th degree of Gemini, having almost 23 degrees north declination, it will be seen without setting at all in almost all parts of the north frigid zone: and therefore the inhabitants of the coast of *Norway*, beyond the city *Nidrosia*, which is called *Drontheim*, as far as the *North Cape*, will be able to observe Venus entering the Sun's disc; and perhaps the ingress of Venus upon the Sun, when rising, will be seen by the *Scotch*, in the northern parts of the kingdom, and by the inhabitants of the *Shetland Isles*, formerly called *Thule*. But at the time when Venus will be nearest the Sun's center, the Sun will be vertical to the northern shores of the bay of *Bengal*, or rather over the kingdom of *Pegu*; and therefore in the adjacent regions, as the Sun, when Venus enters his disc, will be almost four hours toward the east, and as many toward the west when she leaves him,

* The sixth of *June*, according to the New Stile.

the apparent motion of Venus on the Sun will be accelerated by almost double the horizontal parallax of Venus from the Sun; because Venus at that time is

---

* This has been already taken notice of in § **24;** but I shall here endeavour to explain it more at large, together with some of the following part of the Doctor's Essay, by a figure.

In Fig. 1. of Plate XV. let C be the center of the Earth, and Z the center of the Sun. In the right line CvZ, make vZ to CZ as 726 is to 1015 (§ **12).** Let acbd be the Earth, v Venus's place in her orbit at the time of her conjunction with the Sun; and let TSU be the Sun, whose diameter is 31' 42".

The motion of Venus in her orbit is in the direction Nvn and the Earth's motion on its axis is according to the order of the 24 hours placed around it in the figure. Therefore, supposing the mouth of the *Ganges* to be at G, when Venus is at E in her orbit, and to be carried from G to g by the Earth's motion on its axis, while Venus moves from E to e in her orbit; it is plain that the motions of Venus and the Ganges are contrary to each other.

The true motion of Venus in her orbit, and consequently the space she seems to run over on the Sun's disc in any given time, could be seen only from the Earth's center C, which is at rest with respect to its surface. And as seen from C, her path on the Sun would be in the right line TtU; and her motion therein at the rate of four minutes of a degree in an hour. T is the point of the Sun's eastern limb which Venus seems to touch at the moment of her total ingress on the Sun, as seen from C, when Venus is at E in her orbit; and U is the point of the Sun's western limb which she seems to touch at the moment of her beginning of egress from the Sun, as seen from C, when she is at c in her orbit.

When the mouth of the *Ganges* is at m (in revolving through the arc Gmg) the Sun is on its meridian. Therefore, since G and g are equally distant from m at the beginning and ending of the transit, it is plain that the Sun will be as far east of the meridian of the *Ganges* (at G) when the transit begins; as it will be west of the meridian of the same place (revolved from G to g) when the transit ends.

But although the beginning of the transit, or rather the moment of Venus's total ingress upon the Sun at T, as seen from the Earth's center, must be when Venus is at E in her orbit, because she is then seen in the direction of the right line GET; yet at the same instant of time, as seen from the *Ganges* at G, she will be short of her ingress on the Sun, being then seen eastward of him, in the right line GEK, which makes the angle KET (equal to the opposite angle GEC), with the right line CET. This angle is called the angle of Venus's parallax from the Sun, which retards the beginning of the transit as seen from the banks of the Ganges; so that the *Ganges* G, must advance a little farther toward m, and Venus must move on in her orbit from E to R, before she can be seen from G (in the right line GRT) wholly within the Sun's disc at T.

When Venus comes to e in her orbit, she will appear at U, as seen from the Earth's center C, just beginning to leave the Sun; that is, at the beginning of her egress from his western limb: but at the same instant of time, as seen from the *Ganges*, which is then at g, she will be quite clear of the Sun toward the west; being then seen from g in the right line geL, which makes an angle, as UeL (equal to the opposite angle Ceg), with the right line CeU: and this is the angle

carried with a retrograde motion from east to west, while an eye placed upon the Earth's surface is whirled the contrary way, from west to east*.

Supposing the Sun's parallax (as we have said) to be 12½", the parallax of Venus will be 43"; from which subtracting the parallax of the Sun, there will remain 30" at least for the horizontal parallax of Venus from the Sun; and therefore the motion of Venus will be increased 45" at least by that parallax, while she passes over the Sun's disc, in those elevations of the pole which are in places near the tropic, and yet more in the neighbourhood of the equator. Now, Venus at that time will move on the Sun's disc, very nearly at the rate of four minutes of a degree in an hour; and therefore 11 minutes of time at least are to be allowed for 45", or three fourths of a minute of a degree; and by this space of time, the duration of this eclipse, caused by Venus will, on account of the parallax, be shortened. And from this shortening of the time only, we might safely enough draw a conclusion concerning the parallax which we are in search of, provided the diameter of the Sun, and the latitude of Venus, were accurately known. But we cannot expect an exact computation in a matter of such subtilty.

We must endeavour therefore to obtain, if possible, another observation, to be taken in those places where Venus will be in the middle of the Sun's

of Venus's parallax from the Sun, as seen from the *Ganges* at *g*, when she is but just beginning to leave the Sun at *U*, as seen from tile Earth's center *C*.

Here it is plain, that the duration of the transit about the mouth of the *Ganges* (and also in the neighbouring places) will be diminished by about double the quantity of Venus's parallax from the Sun at the beginning and ending of the transit. For Venus must be at *E* in her orbit when she is wholly upon the Sun at *T*, as seen from the Earth's center *C*: but at that time she is short of the Sun, as seen from the *Ganges* at *G*, by the whole quantity of her eastern parallax from the Sun at that time, which is the angle *KET*. [This angle, in fact, is only 23"; though it is represented much larger in the figure, because the Earth therein is a vast deal too big.] Now, as Venus moves at the rate of 4' an hour, she will move 23" in 5 minutes 45 seconds: and, therefore, the transit will begin later by 5 minutes 45 seconds at the banks of the *Ganges* than at the Earth's center.—When the transit is ending at *U*, as seen from the Earth's center at *C*, Venus will be quite clear of the Sun (by the whole quantity of her western parallax from him) as seen from the *Ganges*, which is then at *g*: and this parallax will be 22", equal to the space through which Venus moves in 5 minutes 30 seconds of time: so that the transit will end 5½ minutes sooner as seen from the *Ganges*, than as seen from the Earth's center.

Hence the whole contraction of the duration of the transit at the mouth of the *Ganges* will be 11 minutes 15 seconds of time: for it is 5 minutes 45 seconds at the beginning, and 5 minutes 30 seconds at the end.

disc at midnight; that is, in places under the opposite meridian to the former, or about 6 hours or 90 degrees west of *London*; and where Venus enters upon the Sun a little before its setting, and goes off a little after its rising. And this will happen under the above-mentioned meridian, and where the elevation of the north pole is about 56 degrees; that is, in a part of *Hudson's Bay*, near a place called *Port-Nelson*. For, in this and the adjacent places, the parallax of Venus will increase the duration of the transit by at least six minutes of time; because, while the Sun, from its setting to its rising seems to pass under the pole, those places on the Earth's disc will be carried with a motion from east to west, contrary to the motion of the *Ganges*; that is, with a motion conspiring with the motion of Venus; and therefore Venus will seem to move more slowly on the Sun, and to be longer in passing over his disc *.

If therefore it should happen that this transit should be properly observed by skilful persons at both these places, it is clear, that its duration will be 17 minutes longer, as seen from *Port-Nelson*, than as seen from the *East-Indies*. Nor is it of much consequence (if the *English* shall at that time give any

* In Fig. I. of Plate XV let *aC* be the meridian of the eastern mouth of the *Ganges*; and *bC* the meridian of' *Port-Nelson* at the mouth of *York River* in *Hudson's Bay*, 56° north latitude. As the meridian of the *Ganges* revolves from *a* to *c*, the meridian of *Port-Nelson* will revolve from *b* to *d*: therefore, while the *Ganges* revolves from *G* to *g*, through the arc *Gmg*, *Port-Nelson* revolves the contrary way (as seen from the Sun or Venus) from *P* to *p* through the arc *Pnp*.—Now, as the motion of Venus is from *E* to *e* in her orbit, while she seems to pass over the Sun's disc in the right line *TtU*, as seen from the Earth's center *C*, it is plain that while the motion of the *Ganges* is contrary to the motion of Venus in her orbit, and thereby shortens the duration of the transit at that place, the motion of *Port-Nelson* is the same way as the motion or Venus, and will therefore increase the duration of the transit: which may in some degree be illustrated by supposing, that while a ship is under sail, if two birds fly along the side of the ship in contrary directions to each other, the bird which flies contrary to the motion of the ship will pass by it sooner than the bird will, which flies the same way that the ship moves.

In fine, it is plain by the figure, that the duration of the transit must be longer as seen from Port-Nelson, than as seen from the Earth's center; and longer as seen from the Earth's center, than as seen from the mouth of the *Ganges*.—For *Port-Nelson* must be at *P*, and Venus at *N* in, her orbit, when she appears wholly within the Sun at *T*: and the same place must be at *p*, and Venus at *n*, when she appears, at *U*, beginning to leave the Sun.—The *Ganges* must be at *G*, and Venus at *R*, when she is seen from *C* upon the Sun at *T*; and the same place must be at *g*, and Venus at *r*, when she begins to leave the Sun at *U*, as seen from *g*. So that Venus must move from *N* to *n* in her orbit, while she is seen to pass over the Sun from *Port-Nelson*; from *E* to *e* in passing over the Sun, as seen from the Earth's center; and only from *R* to *r* while she passes over the Sun, as seen from the banks of the *Ganges*.

attention to this affair) whether the observation be made at *Fort-George*, commonly called *Madras*, or at *Bencoolen* on the western shore of the island of *Sumatra*, near the Equator. But if the *French* should be disposed to take any pains herein, an observer may station himself conveniently enough at *Pondicherry* on the west shore of the bay of *Bengal*, where the altitude of the pole is about 12 degrees. As to the *Dutch*, their celebrated mart at *Batavia* will afford them a place of observation fit enough for this purpose, provided they also have but a disposition to assist in advancing, in this particular, the knowledge of the heavens.—And indeed I could wish that many observations of the same phenomenon might be taken by different persons at several places, both that we might arrive at a greater degree of certainty by their agreement, and also lest any single observer should be deprived, by the intervention of clouds, of a sight, which I know not whether any man living in this or the next age will ever see again; and on which depends the certain and adequate solution of a problem the most noble, and at any other time not to be attained to. I recommend it, therefore, again and again, to those curious Astronomers, who (when I am dead) will have an opportunity of observing these things that they would remember this my admonition, and diligently apply themselves with all their might to the making this observation; and I earnestly wish them all imaginable success; in the first place that they may not, by the unseasonable obscurity of a cloudy sky, be deprived of this most desirable sight; and then, that having ascertained with more exactness the magnitudes of the planetary orbits, it may redound to their immortal fame and glory.

We have now shewn, that by this method the Sun's parallax may be investigated to within its five hundredth part, which doubtless will appear wonderful to some. But if an accurate observation be made in each of the places above marked out, we have already demonstrated that the durations of this eclipse made by Venus will differ from each other by 17 minutes of time; that is, upon a supposition that the Sun's parallax is 12½". But if the difference shall be found by observation to be greater or less, the Sun's parallax will be greater or less, nearly in the same proportion. And since 17 minutes of time are answerable to 12½ seconds of solar parallax, for every second of parallax there will arise a difference of more than 80 seconds of time; whence, if we have this difference true to two seconds, it will be certain what the Sun's parallax is to within a 40th part of one second; and therefore his distance will be determined to within its 500dth part at least, if the parallax be not found less than what we have supposed: for 40 times 12½ make 500.

And now I think I have explained this matter fully, and even more than I needed to have done, to those who understand Astronomy: and I would have them take notice, that on this occasion, I have had no regard to the latitude of Venus, both to avoid the inconvenience of a more intricate calculation, which would render the conclusion less evident, and also because the motion of the nodes of Venus is nor yet discovered, nor can be determined but by such conjunctions of the planet with the Sun as this is. For we conclude that Venus will pass 4 minutes below the Sun's center, only in consequence of the supposition that the plane of Venus's orbit is immoveable in the sphere of the fixed stars, and that its nodes remain in the same places where they were found in the year 1639. But if Venus, in the year 1761, should move over the Sun in a path more to the south, it will be manifest that her nodes have moved backward among the fixed stars; and if more to the north, that they have moved forward; and that at the rate of 5½ minutes of a degree in 100 Julian years, for every minute that Venus's path shall be more or less distant than the above said 4 minutes from the Sun's center. And the difference between the duration of these eclipses will be somewhat less than 17 minutes of time, on account of Venus's south latitude; but greater if by the motion of the nodes forward she should pass on the north of the Sun's center.

But for the sake of those, who, though they are delighted with sidereal observations, may not yet have made themselves acquainted with the doctrine parallaxes, I chuse to explain the thing a little more fully by scheme, and also by a calculation somewhat more accurate.

Let us suppose that at *London*, in the year 1761, on the 6th of June, at 15 minutes after V in the morning, the Sun will be in Gemini 15°37', and therefore that at its center the ecliptic is inclined toward the north, in an angle of 6°10': and that the visible path of Venus on the Sun's disc at that time declines to the south, making an angle with the ecliptic of 8°28': then the path of Venus will also be inclined to the south, with respect to the equator, intersecting the parallels of declination at an angle of 2°18'*. Let us

* This was an oversight in the Doctor, occasioned by his placing both the Earth's axis *BCg* (Fig. 2. of Plate XV.) and the Axis of Venus's orbit *CH* on the same side of the axis of

also suppose, that Venus, at the forementioned time, will be at her least distance from the Sun's center, viz. only four minutes to the south; and that every hour she will describe a space of 4 minutes on the Sun, with a retrograde motion. The Sun's semidiameter will be 15'51" nearly, and that of Venus 37½". And let us suppose, for trial's sake; that the difference of the horizontal parallaxes of Venus with the Sun (which we want) is 31", such as it comes out if the Sun's parallax be supposed 12½". Then, on the center C (Plate XV. Fig. 2.) let the little circle AB, representing the Earth's disc, be described, and let its semidiameter CB be 31"; and let the elliptic parallels of 22 and 56 degrees of north latitude (for the *Ganges* and *Port-Nelson*) be drawn within it, in the manner now used by Astronomers for constructing solar eclipses. Let BCg be the meridian in which the Sun is, and to this, let the right line FHG, representing the path of Venus, be inclined at an angle of 2°18'; and let it be distant from the center C 240 such parts, whereof CB is 31. From C let fall the right line CH, perpendicular to FG; and suppose Venus to be at H at 55 minutes after V in the morning. Let the right line FHG be divided into the horary space III IV, IV V, V VI, etc. each equal to CH; that is, to 4 minutes of a degree. Also, let the right line LM be equal to the difference of the apparent semidiameters of the Sun and Venus, which is 15' 13½"; and a circle being described with the radius LM, on a center taken in any point within the little circle AB representing the Earth's disc, will meet the right line FG in a point denoting the time at *London* when Venus shall touch the Sun's limb internally, as seen from the place of the Earth's surface that answers to the point assumed in the Earth's disc. And if a circle be described on the center C, with the radius LM, it will meet the right line FG, in the points F and G; and the spaces FH and GH will be each equal to 14'4", which space Venus will appear to pass over in 3 hours 40 minutes of time at *London*; therefore, F will fall in II hours 15 minutes, and G in IX hours 35 minutes in the morning. Whence it is manifest, that if the magnitude of the Earth, on account of its immense distance, should vanish as it were into a

the ecliptic CK; the former making an angle of 6°10' therewith, and the latter an angle of 8°28'; the difference of which angles is only 2°18'. But the truth is, that the Earth's axis, and the axis of Venus's orbit, will then lie on different sides of the axis of the ecliptic, the former making an angle of 6° therewith, and the latter an angle of 8½°. Therefore, the sum of these angles, which is 14½° (and not their difference 2°18') is the inclination of Venus's visible path to the equator and parallels of declination.

point; or, if being deprived of a diurnal motion, it should always have the Sun vertical to the same point *C*; the whole duration of this eclipse would be 7 hours 20 minutes. But the Earth in that time being whirled through 110 degrees of longitude, with a motion contrary to the motion of Venus, and consequently the abovementioned duration being contracted, suppose 12 minutes, it will come out 7 hours 8 minutes, or 107 degrees, nearly.

Now, Venus will be at *H*, at her least distance from the Sun's center, when in the meridian of the eastern mouth of the *Ganges*, where the altitude of the pole is about 22 degrees. The Sun therefore will be equally distant from the meridian of that place, at the moments of the ingress and egress of the planet, viz.53½ degrees; as the points *a* and *b* (representing that place in the Earth's disc *AB*) are, in the greater parallel, from the meridian *BCg*. But the diameter *cf* of that parallel will be to the distance *ab*, as the square of the radius to the rectangle under the sines of 53½ and 68 degrees; that is, as 1'2" to 46"13"'. And by a good calculation (which, that I may not tire the reader, it is better to omit) I find, that a circle described on *a* as a center, with the radius *LM*, will meet the right line *FH* in the point *M*, at II hours 20 minutes 40 seconds; but that being described round *b* as *a* center, it will meet *HG* in the point *N* at IX hours 29 minutes 22 seconds, according to the time reckoned at *London*: and therefore, Venus will be seen entirely within the Sun at the banks of the *Ganges* for 7 hours 8 minutes 42 seconds: we have then rightly supposed, that the duration will be 7 hours 8 minutes, since the part of a minute here is of no consequence.

But adapting the calculation to *Port-Nelson*, I find, that the Sun being about to set, Venus will enter his disc; and immediately after his rising she will leave the same. That place is carried in the intermediate time through the hemisphere opposite to the Sun, from *c* to *d*, with a motion conspiring with the motion of Venus; and therefore, the stay of Venus on the Sun will be about 4 minutes longer, on account of the parallax; so that it will be at least 7 hours 24 minutes, or 111 degrees of the equator. And since the latitude of the place is 56 degrees, as the square of the radius is to the rectangle contained under the sines 55½ and 34 degrees, so is *AB*, which is 1'2", to *cd*, which is 28"33"'. And if the calculation be justly made, it will appear that a circle described on *c* as a center, with the radius *LM*, will meet the right line *FH* in *O* at II hours 12 minutes 45 seconds; and that such a circle, described on *d* as a center, will meet *HG* in *P*, at IX hours 36 minutes 37 seconds; and therefore the duration at *Port-Nelson* will be 7 hours 23 minutes 52 seconds, which is greater than at the mouth of the *Ganges* by 15 minutes 10 seconds of time. But if Venus should pass over the Sun without having any latitude, the difference would be 18 minutes 40 seconds; and if she should pass 4' north of the Sun's center, the difference would amount to 21 minutes 40 seconds, and will be still greater, if the planet's north latitude be more increased.

From the foregoing hypothesis it follows, that at *London*, when the Sun rises, Venus will have entered his disc; and that, at IX hours 37 minutes in the morning, she will touch the limb of the Sun internally in going off; and lastly, that she will not entirely leave the Sun till IX hours 56 minutes.

It likewise follows from the same hypothesis, that the center of Venus should just touch the Sun's northern limb in the year 1769, on the third of *June*, at XI o'clock at night. So that, on account of the parallax, it will appear in the northern parts of *Norway*, entirely within the Sun, which then does not set to those parts; while, on the coasts of *Peru* and *Chili*, it will seem to travel over a small portion of the disc of the setting Sun; and over that of the rising Sun at the *Molucca Islands*, and in their neighbourhood.—But if the nodes of Venus be found to have a retrograde motion (as there is some reason to believe from some later observations they have) then Venus will be seen every where within the Sun's disc; and will afford a much better method for finding the Sun's parallax, by almost the greatest difference in the duration of these eclipses that can possibly happen.

But how this parallax may be deduced from observations made some-where in the East-Indies, in the year 1761, both of the ingress and egress of Venus, and compared with those made in its going off with us, namely, by applying the angles of a triangle given in specie to the circumference of three equal circles, shall be explained on some other occasion.

Reproduced from:
Ferguson, James, *Astronomy Explained Upon Sir Isaac Newton's Principles, and made easy to those who have not studied Mathematics*, Sixth Edition, London, 1778

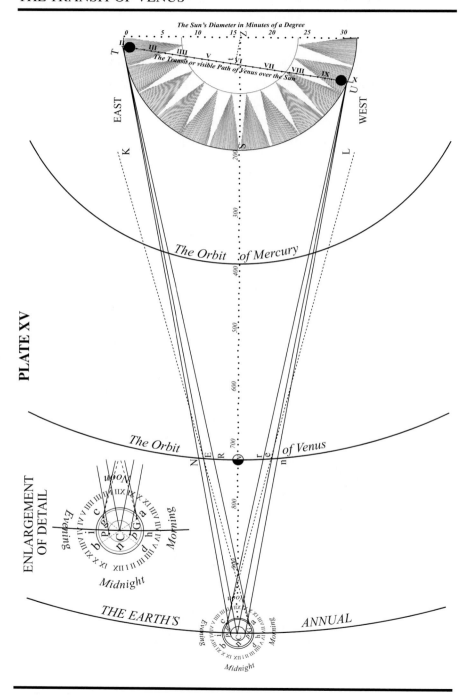

PLATE XV

PLATE XV continued

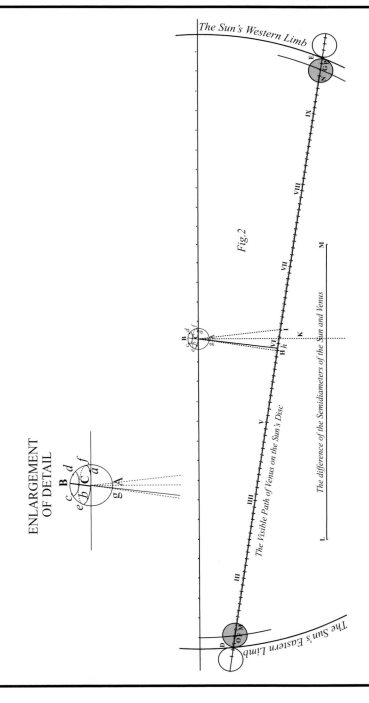

ENLARGEMENT
OF DETAIL

Fig. 2

The Sun's Western Limb

The Sun's Eastern Limb

The Visible Path of Venus on the Sun's Disc

The difference of the Semidiameters of the Sun and Venus

INDEX

A

Airy, George 142, 166
Al-Battani 71
al-Ma'mum 34
Alexander the Great 19
Alexandria 24
Alexandria, Library of 23, 32
Almagest 31, 34–36
Alphonsine Tables 35, 38, 45
Alphonso X 35
Anaxagoras 19, 22
angular measures 22–23
Anson, George 147
Aristarchus 20–22, 86
Aristotle 19, 27, 29–30, 32, 34, 176
Aspects of the planets 40
Averroes (Ibn Rushd) 71

B

Babylonian astronomy 16
Bachazek, Martin 75
Ball, Robert 9–12, 15
Banks, Joseph 145
Barberini, Maffeo (Urban VIII) 69
Bayly, William 145
Bellarmino, Cardinal 68
Benatky Castle 49, 53
Bevis, John 144, 145

black-drop effect 126–127, 133, 149–150, 157
Bradley, James 125
Bruno, Giordano 51

C

Calendar, Gregorian 67
Calendar, Julian 67
Calton Hill Observatory 160
Cape Observatory 159
Cartier, Jacques 147
Cassini de Thury 128, 139, 154
Cassini, Gian Domenico 101
Chambers, Sir William 151
Chappe d'Auteroche, Jean-Baptiste 120, 131–133, 138–140, 153
Christian VII, King of Denmark 140
Clavius, Christopher 64, 66–68
Cleomedes 24–25
comets 28, 49
Commentariolus (of Copernicus) 40
conjunction 39
constellations 16
Cook, James 13, 145, 147–151, 153, 184
Copernicus, Nicolas 35–43, 71, 74, 77, 80
Crabtree, William 80–81, 84–85, 88–89

D

De Revolutionibus Orbium
    Coelestium (of Copernicus) 43
dead-reckoning 97
degree of latitude, size of 113–115
Delisle, Joseph-Nicolas 119–120,
    128
Delisle's mappemonde 120–122
Delisle's method 119–120
Demainbray, Stephen 151
Dixon, Jeremiah 122–127, 145
Doz, Vicente de 138
Dreyer, J.L.E. 25
Dun Echt Observatory 161
Dunsink Observatory 9–13
Dymond, Joseph 145, 153

E

Earth, size of 23–25, 113–116
Earth, sphericity of 18
eclipse, of Jupiter's moons 101–102
ellipse 55
elongation of planets 31, 39, 44, 65
Encke, Johann Franz 155
epicycle 32–33, 37–39
equant 33
Eratosthenes 24–26, 114
Eros (Planet DQ) 168–171

F

Fabricius, Johannes 76
Ferguson, James 123, 144, 204
Flamsteed, John 101, 104, 106, 108,
    165–166
Fortunate Islands (Canaries) 98
Foucault, Léon 156
Fouchy, Grandjean de 139

G

Galileo Galilei 60–71, 74

Galileo spacecraft 177–178
Gallet, Jean Charles 108
Gama, Vasco da 147
Gassendi, Pierre 76–77, 97
Gerard of Cremona 35
Giese, Tiedemann 42
Gill, David 159–165
Gill, Isobel 161, 163–165
Goldstone radar installation 175–176
Grant, Robert 155
Green, Charles 145–146, 148–149,
    151, 153
Green, Paul 173–174
Greenwich (prime) meridian 98–99
Gregory, James 108

H

Hadrian, Emperor 34
Halley, Edmond 103–109, 112,
    115–119, 126, 133–134,
    166, 204
Hansen, Peter 155
Harkness, William 179
Harrison, John 101
Harun al-Rashid 34
Haystack radar installation 177
heliocentric theory 37–38, 65
heliometer 162–163
Hell, Maximilian 140–144, 153
Hevelius, Johannes 84, 89
Hipparchus 86
Hooke, Robert 106, 178
Hoole 81
Hornsby, Thomas 144, 146, 153–155
Horrocks, Jeremiah 10, 13, 78–91,
    96–97, 133
Hoskyns, Sir John 116
Huygens, Christian 101

I

inferior conjunction 39

J

Jodrell Bank radio observatory 175–176
Jones, Harold Spencer 171
Jupiter, moons of 63–64, 101–102

K

Kepler, Johannes 49–60, 74–77, 166
Kepler's Laws 58–59, 112, 153, 159
Kerguelen Island 15
Kew Observatory (Richmond) 151–152
King Charles II 101, 103, 115
King George III 151–152

L

Lalande, Joseph-Jerome de 134–136, 142
Lansberg, Philip Van 79–80
latitude 98–99
Le Gentil, Joseph-Hyacinthe-Jean-Baptiste 120, 128–129, 134, 136–138
Le Roy, Pierre 101
Lindsay, Lord (Earl of Crawford) 161–162
Linke, Felix 167–168
Littrow, Carl Ludwig 142–143
longitude 98–99
Longitude, Board of 99
Longomontanus, Christian Severinus 53, 77, 80
Lucretius 28
luminous ring effect 127, 140
Luther, Martin 40–41

M

Macclesfield, Earl of 122, 127
Maestlin, Michael 50, 56
Magellan, Ferdinand 99, 136

Mars, motion of 31, 53–54
Maskelyne, Nevil 122, 125, 127, 133, 144–145, 149
Mason, Charles 122–127
Maxwell, James Clerk 160
Medina, Salvador de 138
Mercury, transit of 75–77, 107
meridian 98
Millstone Hill radar installation 171–176
Moon, eclipse of 19, 21–22, 139
Moon, phases of 19–20, 66
Moon, sphericity of 19
Moon, surface of 62
Moore, Sir Jonas 106, 108

N

Narratio Prima (of Copernicus) 42
Nautical Almanac 125
Newcomb, Simon 143, 156–157, 169
Newton, Isaac 88, 102, 178
nodes 72, 92–93
nodes, line of 76
Noël, Alexandre-Jean 138–139
Norwood, Richard 113–114
novas 47–48

O

observation precautions 10, 181
Oldenburg, Henry 104, 165
opposition 39–40
Osiander, Andreas 42

P

parallax 26
parallax of Mars 158–159, 162
pendulum clock 100
pendulum, length of 102
Perry, Stephen 15
Pettengill, Gordon 175
photography of asteroids 167–

168, 170
photography of transits 157–158
Piazzi, Giuseppe 168
Piazzi Smyth, Charles 160
Picard, Jean 114–115
Pigafetta 99
Pingré, Alexandre-Gui 120, 129–130, 134, 136, 140, 144
Plato 23
Pliny 25
Price, Robert 173–174
Prime Meridian 98
Ptolemy, Claudius 31–34, 43, 45, 77, 86
Ptolemy Evergetes 23
Ptolemy Soter 23

R

radar 171–177
Radcliffe Observatory, Oxford 162
Ray, John 116
Reinhold, Erasmus 43
retrograde motion 31–32, 38
Rheticus, Georg Joachim 41–42
Richer, Jean 102–103
Royal Greenwich Observatory 12, 99–101, 118, 133, 145–147, 159
Royal Observatory of Paris 101, 133
Rudolphine Tables 59–60, 80
Rumovsky, Stepan 153

S

Sacrobosco 66, 79
Sajnovics, Joannes 140
Schönberg, Nicholas 40
Seven Years' War 121
Shapiro, Irwin 177
Short, James 144, 147
Shovell, Admiral Sir Cloudisley 99

sidereal period 73
Socrates 23
Solander, Daniel Carl 149
solar parallax 26–27, 86–87, 133, 153, 177, 196
Somerville, Mary 156
South, Sir James 11
spheres, celestial 29–30, 48–49, 51
Sputnik 1 177
St. Helena 103, 105, 122, 127
Stevens, Robert 175
Stone, E.J. 156, 159
Strabo 25
sunspots 76
superior conjunction 39
Syene 24
synodic period 73

T

Tahiti, discovery of 147
Thomson, David 160
Towneley, Richard 165
Transits of Venus, contacts 95
Transits of Venus, dates of 92, 116–117, 179–81
triangulation 114–116
Tupman, G.L. 157
Tycho Brahe 45–49, 52–54, 59, 152, 166

U

Urania Observatory, Berlin 167–168
Uraniborg 49, 53
US Naval Observatory 156, 161

V

Vedel, Anders 46
Venus, phases of 65–66
Victor, Walter 175

W

Waddington, Robert 122, 127
Wales, William 145, 153
Wallis, Samuel 147–149
Watzenrode, Lucas 35
Wendelin, Gottfried 86
Willoughby, Francis 116
Winnecke 156
Witt, Gustav 167–170
Worthington, John 89
Wren, Sir Christopher 116

Y

Yevpatoriya radar installation 176